"Catherine provides an excellent framework to create and grow an aesthetic practice. She thoughtfully details each step of the process from intake, to consultation through post-operative care. Her paradigm shifts the mindset from medical practice to top-tier service provider. **This guide book is required reading for all members of our team.**"

**DAVID KAUFMAN, MD, FACS**

Kaufman and Clark Plastic Surgery, Folsom, CA

"This outstanding book is an excellent overview and resource regarding marketing an aesthetic practice. It begins where marketing should begin, with the patients themselves. Patient comments and an excellent survey reveal what the patients want and don't want. There are many practical tips on patient relations, rapport building, the consultation process and decision-making. Emphasis is placed where it should be, on internal marketing strategies. External marketing is put in excellent perspective and the author makes it clear it should not be even attempted until the infrastructure is in place and the internal marketing strategies have been fully implemented. **This outstanding piece by Catherine Maley, MBA, should be a welcomed addition to any aesthetic physicians in early practice but for mature practices as well.** It has certainly been helpful to me to have the pleasure of reviewing this book.

**FERDINAND F. BECKER MD, FACS**

*"The Best Doctors in America," "America's Top Doctors," "Guide to America's Top Physicians"* and *"America's Cosmetic Doctors and Dentists"*

Private Practice, Vero Beach, FL

It was great to
meet you in Vegas!
Let's talk soon!

Catherine

# YOUR
# **AESTHETIC**
# PRACTICE

## a complete guide

ISBN: 9781613648018

Library of Congress Control Number: 2007932272

# YOUR
# **AESTHETIC**
# PRACTICE

### a complete guide

## What Your
## Patients Are
## Saying

**Catherine Maley, MBA**

# DEDICATION

This book is dedicated to the many physicians who have helped me throughout my career by offering insight into your world of aesthetic medicine.

I sincerely appreciate you sharing your vision, interests, challenges and concerns with me so I could, in turn, help other physicians.

I appreciate your support,

*Catherine*

# Find Out How You Stack Up
# Against The Top Aesthetic Practices

### How Do You Compare To Top Aesthetic Practices?
### Download Your FREE Instant Marketing Checklist
### Today!

### Go to
### www.CosmeticImageMarketing.com
### to discover how you compare to
### the top aesthetic practices.

### Call (877) 339-8833 or Visit www.CosmeticImageMarketing.com
### To learn More!

# TABLE OF CONTENTS

# FOREWORD

Effective practice management strategies and sharp marketing imperatives are two essential components to growing and sustaining a successful practice. Unfortunately, these basic tenets of a medical practice are poorly represented in our school curriculums and in fact often are denigrated as beneath the importance of the higher order Hippocrates-Osler guided servants of the population that is to be our calling. But the DNA of most physicians and at the basic core of our training is the bud of marketing and practice management. Skills such as deductive reasoning, affability and selflessness are inherent to most physicians. Additionally, we learn how to market ourselves as we strive for good grades on clinical rotations, request recommendations and seek out jobs. We also learn management skills during our senior resident years as we delegate and coordinate junior residents and medical students to take care of many sick patients. However somewhere along the line we become so focused on our textbooks, procedures and medical world that we may lose sight of how the rest of the world thinks. The language we speak and the initiatives that motivate us may not be common to the staff we employ or the patients we treat. We could all use a refresher course from time to time and a little guidance on how to better communicate with our staff and patients.

In today's healthcare environment practice management and marketing skills are important no matter your specialty. The Internet has altered the way we practice medicine and the way patients research their medical care regardless if it is a neurogenic tumor or a hang nail. Cosmetic medicine, however, is a bit different in that procedures are completely elective and patients have many more options in who they choose to provide their care. Cosmetic physicians would be wise to understand a little bit of retail flair. It is essential to make your patient or in this case also a customer happy. If your office does not provide the experience they are looking for, they will not come back. ***Your Aesthetic Practice: a complete guide* hits the nail on the head with incredibly important and essential strategies for building, fueling and excelling in a cosmetic practice.** Difficult concepts are made easy to understand. Providing relevant and immediately implement able tips, Catherine helps you to get patients in the door and then offers pearls for ensuring their experiences is great. This book is a great addition for those in cosmetic medicine but is applicable for all those in the practice of medicine. Additionally, I would recommend it to office managers and medical residents. The demand for cosmetic medicine is exploding and with no end in site. For those physicians who learn to optimize their office efficiency and maximize their patients' happiness, a lifelong and rewarding career waits.

### STEVEN H. DAYAN, MD, FACS

SDMD Facial Plastic Surgery - Chicago, IL
Clinical Assistant Professor, University of Illinois
Enhance Educational Foundation - Executive Director
Medical Director - DeNova Research
President - True University
President - If Marketing

# INTRODUCTION

This book was written to help you, the aesthetic physician, grow a cosmetic practice in today's dynamic and challenging marketplace.

Think of this resource as your own personal marketing consultant at your service. Included are useful ideas and insights to grow your revenues and help you:

- understand the buying habits of aesthetic patients
- convert more consultations to booked procedures
- increase your word-of-mouth referrals through satisfied patients
- beat your competition
- work smarter, not harder
- keep your overhead costs down
- stop wasting money on ineffective marketing efforts

As you probably know you are participating in one of the most exciting and unique industries in our history. Aesthetic medicine has turned into a lucrative, multi-billion industry that continues to grow. This phase of exploding growth will continue thanks to:

- Baby Boomers (1/3 of our population or 80 million people) are not aging gracefully. They want to look as good as they feel and they have the disposable income to gain/regain their youthful appearance;

- Today's beauty-obsessed culture;

- Media fueling the desire to look younger by reporting the latest advancements in cosmetic enhancement – especially since a majority of their viewers, readers and listening audiences are Baby Boomers;

- TV shows that take away the stigma of cosmetic enhancement so aesthetic patients are more likely to speak openly to their friends, family and colleagues about cosmetic procedures they've had;

- Changes in managed care reimbursement to motivate health care professionals to look to the cosmetic enhancement industry for other sources of revenue;

- Medi-spas opening daily owned by core as well as non-core specialties, entrepreneurs, venture capitalists and business people; and

- New, less-invasive technologies increase the interest and numbers of consumers who want to look their best with little or no downtime and no telltale signs of having had a procedure performed.

Given the above, I congratulate you for maneuvering through the complexities of growing an aesthetic practice. It takes a certain skill set and more to rise above your competitors. An excellent aesthetic physician with skill, advanced technology and a comfortable office is not always enough to build a successful aesthetic practice in today's competitive climate. It takes many nuances working together to make it a truly successful aesthetic practice. It has become imperative to attract your preferred patient through strategic and professional promotion and marketing as outlined in this resource.

The aesthetic patient today can be a fickle consumer. Truly understanding their needs and wants helps you better address them so they choose you over your competitors, stay loyal to you and refer their friends, family and colleagues. One of the best ways to gain that understanding is to listen to the patient's voice. Throughout this book you will "hear" their thoughts and decision-making processes.

Stories from patients surveyed will be shared to give you pearls to assist in the successful launch or continuation of your aesthetic practice. You will also find many easy-to-execute marketing strategies to help you market your products and services effectively and professionally.

I sincerely hope this book reassures you that you are currently doing many things right and that it offers you guidance to improve certain aspects of your practice and brings the best return on your investment of time, money and resources.

Good luck to you and I welcome your feedback.

Email me directly: Catherine@CosmeticImageMarketing.com

*Catherine*

**Catherine Maley**, MBA
President & Senior Marketing Strategist
Cosmetic Image Marketing

I

# RESEARCH

Aesthetic patient interviews were conducted with 75 patients for this book. These patients had both surgical and non-surgical procedures for some type of cosmetic enhancement including injectables and laser treatments. The goal was to determine the aesthetic patients' thought processes, decision-making styles and general feelings about their aesthetic physician, the practice and the process.

The majority of patients interviewed were female as they still make up 85-90% of the aesthetic population; however, male perceptions are also included. Those interviewed came from a diverse group of patients throughout the country in both large cities and smaller towns. The median age was 44 years old.

HIPAA regulations require names and references be changed to retain their anonymity.

---

*Key points, patient comments and helpful resources will be noted in shaded boxes throughout this book.*

---

# STACEY'S STORY

*"I was ready to turn back the clock. I knew I was looking older and friends kept asking me if I was tired. I was a single professional with a stressful job and it was showing. I wanted to refresh my look to not only feel better about myself but also to stay competitive – both professionally and socially.*

*Since I had been getting Botox, fillers and IPL for a couple of years from the nurse at a plastic surgeon's office, I spoke with her about getting my eyes done and she highly recommended her plastic surgeon. I also asked other friends and did some research on the Internet and went on three consultations. I actually picked the plastic surgeon whose nurse I had been going to since I was most comfortable there and really liked him.*

*At the consultation the surgeon was professional, knowledgeable and experienced. He was older and had done many of these procedures because he showed me a huge book of his before/after photos. He spent a long time with me, which was impressive since I knew he was busy. His thoroughness made me more comfortable and he even suggested an additional procedure. I agreed since he was spending so much time with me. I felt like he gave me all of my options but let me choose what I wanted. I was also impressed with his measuring devices, since again, it showed how thorough and precise he was.*

*The surgery went well and my recovery wasn't bad. I should tell you, however, that although I loved my result, I never saw him again after surgery. He had his fellow and his nurse handle my post-op care. While I got great care from them, I would have liked to see the surgeon again. I felt dismissed and have not told as many people about him as I would have had he followed up with me personally – at least once."*

— Stacey, 41 years old - Botox, Fillers and Bleph

# SURVEY RESULTS – STATISTICAL AND ANECDOTAL

## 1. Why did you have a cosmetic enhancement procedure?

39%     To look younger

38%     To look better

11%     To find romance

6%      Recently divorced and wanted change

4%      Finally had the money

2%      Other*

*stay competitive
*saw a friend's result and wanted the same
*wanted to look good for wedding/holidays
*fight aging process
*felt more confident when better looking

## 2. What kind of research did you do beforehand?

45%     Spoke with Friends, Family or Colleagues*

23%     TV

16%     Internet

11%     None+

3%      Magazines

2%      Other#

*talking with their friends was considered research
+just went with one word-of-mouth referral
#Other included attending events

## 3. How long did it take you to decide to go through with the procedure?

1-2 years: Surgical procedures*

30 minutes – 2 weeks: Minimally invasive procedures+

*This was from the time they considered to the time they booked. However, when they decided for sure, the procedure was booked and performed within weeks if possible.

+Minimally-invasive procedures were more impulsive and the majority of patients wanted to discuss and have them performed at the same time as the consultation.

## 4. How did you hear about the physician?

| | |
|---|---|
| 35% | Friend/Family |
| 32% | Colleague* |
| 13% | Print/TV media |
| 8% | Internet |
| 5% | Yellow Pages |
| 3% | Hair Salon/Spa |
| 2% | Other physician |
| 2% | Direct Mail |

*Perhaps because so much time is spent at work versus home, colleagues have become close confidants.

## 5. Number of consultations you went on before deciding?

| | | |
|---|---|---|
| 39% | 1 | Consultation* |
| 28% | 2 | Consultations |
| 33% | 3+ | Consultations |

*of the 39%, 82% were referrals from friends, family or colleagues

## 6. How important was it in your decision the staff be courteous, informative, friendly and caring?

91%   A lot

8%   Some

1%   Didn't care

Note: It was mentioned several times that patients were not treated kindly and would have left the practice; however, they liked the physician so much, they stayed in spite of the staff.

Note: The staff's demeanor mattered most when a friend or colleague did not refer the prospective patient since they did not have any prior reference to the practice.

Note: It was mentioned several times the staff smelled like smoke, which was a turn-off and affected the image of a "clean" office.

## 7. Did waiting times affect your decision one way or the other?

52%   Waited less than 20 minutes and were satisfied

38%   Waited too long but were happy with the result*

9%   Waited too long and did not return again

1%   Walked out after waiting too long

*Note: Long waiting times were a reoccurring complaint but usually forgivable IF they got a good result.

## 8. How important were the aesthetics of the office?

78%     Very Important

20%     Somewhat Important

2%      Not Important

Note:   The office's cleanliness and tidiness was important to almost everyone; however, the actual aesthetics of the office were more important to the prospective patient who was not referred to the practice.

Other comments about the office from those surveyed:

*"If they are conscientious about their office, they will be conscientious about my procedure."*

*"It reflects the physician's own personality and value system but is not the end-all deciding factor in choosing him."*

*"The office represents the doctor and should say good things about him/her."*

*"A nice office shows he has class and pride in his work."*

*"I would expect to pay more in a really nice office."*

*"I was intimidated by the office – it was way too pretentious."*

*"I just care about parking and getting in and out easily."*

*"A nice office makes me feel he's creative, artistic and of quality."*

*"When I enter a calm, aesthetically-pleasing atmosphere, it relaxes me and makes me feel as if I'm in good hands."*

## 9. How important was the physician's printed materials – business cards, letterhead, in-house signage, patient information packets and media PR?

43%    Very Important

40%    Somewhat Important

17%    Not Important

Note: It was more important when the patient was calling around and requesting information be sent to their homes. They responded more positively when the materials were professional and informative and showcased the physician as an expert.

Other comments from those surveyed:

*"The doctor's materials are important to show he's creative, professional, credible, knowledgeable and up-to-date."*

*"The entire package of information is important because if he pays attention to this detail, he will pay attention to my details."*

*"I don't care about his 15 minutes of fame – I just care that he will do a good job for me."*

*"His printed materials show he is savvy, up-to-date and innovative."*

*"I was impressed that he had published articles and was on TV."*

## 10. Were you charged for your consultation? Did that affect your decision?

55%    Charged

45%    Not Charged

Note: Patients who were referred by a friend, family or colleague were much more willing to pay for the consultation than those who were shopping multiple doctors. And, patients were more willing to pay a consultation fee when they were discussing facial surgery as opposed to minimally-invasive procedures.

Other comments from those surveyed:

> *"The physician should value his time and charge for it."*

> *"It seems desperate to me if consultations are free."*

> *"I would not have gone to him if he had charged me a consultation fee."*

## 11. Did you prefer the physician wear scrubs, suit/tie, white lab coat and did it affect your decision in any way?

61%     White lab coat

20%     Suit and Tie

10%     Scrubs

9%     Don't Care

Note: Patients who were referred by a friend, family or colleague didn't care as much what the physician wore. However, patients cared more that whatever they wore was of high quality, clean, ironed, spot-free and nice-fitting.

## 12. How were you greeted and treated by the physician and did it matter?

95%   Handshake

92%   Looked in eye

82%   Sat face-to-face with no barriers such as desk

68%   Small talk first

56%   Listened

52%   Seemed genuinely interested and concerned about me as a person and as a patient

28%   Felt disingenuous and phony

Other comments from those surveyed:

*"He asked me about my kids and I really liked that."*

*"He talked all about him and nothing about me."*

*"He told me he was attracted to the Asian culture and I liked that since I'm Asian and felt he understood me."*

*"She made me comfortable with her as a person before she jumped into the medical stuff."*

*"He addressed my specific concerns which I appreciated."*

*"He repeated back what I said so I felt he really heard me."*

*"He kept telling me what I wanted instead of listening to what I "really" wanted."*

### 13. How much time did the physician spend with you in your consultation?

54%    Less than 30 minutes

41%    30-60 minutes

5%    More than 1 hour

Note: The better the staff, the less time the physician had to spend with the patient during the consultation. And the bigger the procedure the more time was needed for the patient to speak with the physician one-on-one.

Other comments from those surveyed:

*"I was so impressed the busy physician spent so much time with me. It showed me he was thorough and cared about me."*

*"He spent so much time with me, I wondered if he had any other patients to see and if he was busy enough."*

*"My physician was so thorough that he scheduled another consultation with me to be sure I had all of my questions answered and I really liked that thoroughness."*

*"He was in and out so fast, I felt like I was on an assembly line."*

### 14. General Comments about the consultation from those surveyed:

*"He was very thorough and measured things with a precise tool so I felt like he was a true perfectionist and would give me the best result."*

*"He was so clinical and technical that he lost me early on. I didn't care how he was going to do it; I just wanted a smaller nose."*

*"He was so arrogant and didn't care about me as a person so I didn't bother asking him any questions. I also didn't bother to schedule surgery and went to someone much more personable."*

*"I really liked one of the physicians I visited; however, he was so thorough and gave me so many choices I got confused. I had to tell him I would need to think it over. While I was thinking it over, my girlfriend told me about another surgeon whom I visited, connected with and scheduled my surgery with because he listened to what I wanted. He showed me results of other patients similar to me and kept it simple."*

*"He had really bad breath and that was a huge turn-off."*

Note: Several patients felt "oversold" during their consultation. The patients who asked were happy getting the physician's opinion. It was the unsolicited feedback from the physician that left the patients feeling oversold. Many felt they didn't need so much so soon.

## 15. Do you prefer a private surgical suite in the physician's office, an out-patient surgical center or a hospital?

68%   Physician's private surgical suite

22%   Hospital or out-patient surgical center*

10%   No Preference

Other comments from those surveyed:

*"I liked the privacy and convenience of the physician's surgical suite."*

*"I felt safer in the hospital."*

*"Hospitals have germs, infections and grumpy staff."*

*"I got much better service in my physician's surgical suite than I ever would have gotten at a big hospital."*

* 22% had a preference for the hospital setting or surgical center versus the physician's private surgical suite. However, if other offices prepped them and explained the various pros and cons of each setting and what to ask, they were more concerned about:

**Accreditation:** of the facility by the American Association for the Accreditation of Ambulatory Plastic Surgery Facilities (AAAPSF) or the Accreditation Association for Ambulatory Health Care (AAAHC) or state-certified, etc.

**Anesthesia:** type to be used and the differences between general and local anesthesia. The public has now heard enough horror stories about people dying under general anesthesia and local has its pros such as less bruising, less downtime, no risk, etc.

**Anesthesiologist:** or who was administering the anesthesia; i.e., surgeon, nurse, anesthesiologist, etc.

**Emergency:** how things would be handled if something did go wrong.

## 16. How did the physician set expectations?

82%     Before/after photos

74%     Hand, mirror, cotton swab

28%     Patient testimonials (staff included)

18%     Call other patients

12%     Drawing free style

8%      Computer imaging or skin analysis tools

Note:  96% would have liked computer imaging or skin analysis

## 17. Rank the importance of each criterion in making your decision:

1. 58% Physician's reputation, credentials, confidence in ability

2. 28% Price

3. 8%  Staff

4. 4%  Location

5. 2%  Facility

Note: These numbers varied depending on the types of procedures – minimally invasive versus surgical. The less invasive, the more price, staff and location were the deciding factors; however, reputation was always important.

## 18. How did the physician follow-up after surgery and how important was that to you?

22%    Received call from physician

55%    Received call from staff*

21%    Did not receive any follow-up call

2%    Were personally visited at home by the physician*

*Of those that received a call from staff, 82% would have preferred the physician call. Those visited at home referred several patients since they were so impressed with the doctor's concern for their recovery. And the more invasive the surgery or procedure, the more the patient wanted to speak to the physician, especially to reassure they would be happy with the result after they got through the recovery process.

## 19. Did the physician follow-up with flowers, fruit and/or thank you card and how important was that?

98%    Did not receive anything afterwards

2%    Received flowers

1%    Received thank you card

Note: 86% would have appreciated receiving something to thank them and to show the practice cared about them.

## 20. Were the physician and staff still friendly and attentive at your follow-up appointments?

64%    Felt they were treated the same

28%    Never met with or saw the physician again

8%    Felt they were treated rudely and dismissively

Other comments from those surveyed:

*"I never saw the doctor again and it made me feel as if I was just another surgery."*

*"The physician wanted to see me back for periodic follow-ups and that made me feel cared for."*

*"The office staff was always so happy to see me; they were like old friends."*

*"The surgeon was actually curt with me and that has kept me from referring others to him."*

## 21. Comments from those surveyed about: complications, dissatisfaction and follow-up:

It came up several times the patient felt uncomfortable discussing dissatisfaction with their physician since they were not being well received. In many instances, the physician became defensive and standoffish. Some even had trouble seeing their surgeons again since they were "always in surgery" when the patient wanted to schedule follow up time to discuss their concerns.

The physicians who actually listened to the patient's concerns and did something about them fared the best and received a majority of the referrals.

## 22. Have you recommended the physician? If so, to how many friends, family and colleagues?

86%    Referred at least two other people to that practice

9%    Did not refer others to that physician because they were dissatisfied

5%    Did not tell anyone they had anything done

Note: The hair stylists were the largest referral source. They referred 100-250 patients to their favorite physicians and surgeons.

## 23. Would you like to have your before/after photos and would you show them to others?

82%    Wanted their before/after photos

76%    Would show them to others

18%    Did not want their photos and would not show them to anyone

## 24. Would you have more cosmetic enhancement? Why or why not?

98%    Yes

2%    Maybe

Note: Nobody said they would never do it again.

Other comments from those surveyed:

*"I don't mind getting older but I do mind looking old."*

*"I want to turn back the clock."*

*"I will fight this aging process to the end!"*

*"I want my "pre-kids" figure back."*

*"I want to look in the mirror and feel good about what I see."*

*"I'm proud of staying in great shape and want my face to reflect my body."*

*"I feel more confident when I look good."*

## 25. How do you feel about physicians advertising and marketing?

### Marketing

Patients surveyed said they were interested in hearing from their physician periodically. They wanted information about what was new in the office as well as new technologies, procedures and treatments in the industry to help them look their best. They saw this more as education than as marketing when the correspondence was informative. They also appreciated hearing about special events and promotions happening throughout the year.

### Advertising

Patients surveyed about physician advertising offered different responses. If the advertising was more informative than "gimmicky," most patients liked to see their physician in the newspaper or the social magazines. This seemed to confirm they picked the right physician. It also gave the physician some recognition with prospective patients who saw the physician's name and photo in a publication. Hearing the physician's name elsewhere led to multiple exposures and helped them choose one physician over the others. They also got good name recognition and their patients were impressed when they were seen in the high-end publications.

If physicians, however, were regularly promoting their practice and discounting their services, several patients questioned why their physician would do so much external advertising if they were so great. They saw this as a desperate measure for the physician to "woo" new patients.

> *"I just love my doctor and his staff. They feel like family to me and I would never go anywhere else."*
>
> — *Connie, 42 years old - Injectables*

# II

# THE VALUE OF
# ONE PATIENT

A successful aesthetic practice is built one patient at a time. It's the complex network of personal relationships and individual interactions over time bringing you the referrals and financial rewards of a truly successful aesthetic practice.

To understand the revenues involved, a lifetime case study was completed for "Sue the aesthetic patient." Sue is a real patient of a plastic surgeon in practice for 16 years.

Sue started going to the practice in her mid 30's for minimally invasive procedures. She enjoyed the staff, had a great experience every visit and liked this doctor's results. Because she was treated so well and the office kept in touch with her through newsletters and special promotions, she told her friends, family and colleagues about the practice. Not only did some also start going to this physician, they were members of the media, high-end spa owners and businesswomen. They were able to put the physician in front of hundreds of other like-minded women. They also visited this physician when they were ready for cosmetic enhancement and referred their friends, family and colleagues and so on and so on.

> *During Sue's lifetime, she has been worth more than $40,000 to the physician personally with her own procedures and another $98,000 in referrals to his practice from her friends, family and colleagues.*
>
> *The word-of-mouth, instant credibility and additional referrals were priceless.*

Please remember and remind your staff every patient interaction is a potential goldmine. You want to take the time to treat your patients with the same respect and generosity as your own close friends or family members.

Thank your patients for referrals so they feel appreciated. Stay in touch with them throughout the years. Circumstances change - life changes – people change. You want to be there for them during those stages of life so they turn to you when they are ready for aesthetic enhancement next week, next month or next year.

## WHAT DOES YOUR AESTHETIC PATIENT REALLY WANT?

> *"The best way to get what you want in life is to give enough other people what they want."*
>
> — *Zig Ziglar*

What do your aesthetic patients *really* want? Could you book more procedures if you knew what was driving them to seek your services in the first place?

The top needs stated in the survey were:

- "I need to stay competitive in the business world."

- "I want to look as good as I feel."

- "I want to still matter."

- "I want to like what I see in the mirror."

- "I'm newly single and want to feel pretty."

- "I'm going to a class reunion and want to make my old boyfriend jealous."

- "I came into some cash and have always wanted to fix this."

- "I'm so sick of looking at (blank) in the mirror and am ready to change it."

- "I have always wanted to improve (blank) and I now have the time and money."

- "I want to do something special just for me."

These are the needs they are able to articulate out loud. But there are underlying emotional needs that need to be addressed. They might not be able to verbalize them but they are most likely also looking for feelings of prestige, freedom, justice, status, love, security, recognition, happiness and time. If you can pinpoint their particular emotional needs and address them, you have turned a prospective consumer into your patient.

> *Your patients want to feel better about themselves and their lives. They are buying hope and happiness. Hope that you will make them look better. Hope their lives will improve. Hope they will feel more happiness. And hope they will feel better about themselves.*

Since these patients don't NEED your services - they WANT them - they will choose you to enhance their appearance only if they trust you and believe you will give them what they want. On the flip side they *don't want* feelings of regret, buyer's remorse or dissatisfaction.

The aesthetic patient is expecting the following from you:

- Your understanding and compassion
- Your undivided attention
- Personalized service
- Fast delivery of service
- Well trained and polite staff
- Professional image
- To get more than promised
- Minimal wait times
- Clear understanding of services and costs
- Fair pricing
- Prompt return calls
- Your telephone answered quickly and professionally
- Non-rushed experience

Women especially like attention and need to know you care about them as a person as well as their comfort and satisfaction. Aesthetic patients want to be heard. They want to know you are listening to them.

You want to address their hopes, wants, needs, fears, concerns, disappointments and expectations. It's important to hear what matters most to your patients and why. Then you want to do what you can to give them what they want within reason. That's how you build trust and loyalty with your patients.

> "He was so caring and interested in me as a person. I was already pre-sold on him thanks to my hair stylist but his caring nature closed the deal."
>
> — Barbara, 44 years old - Bleph and Botox

# WHAT MEN WANT

Men make up roughly 10-15% of the current market and that number is increasing. It's important to know their needs and wants in order to be able to cater to them.

Men's motivations are not too different from women's. They also want to look good and stay competitive and marketable in the work place as well as on the social scene. They may also be a baby boomer and this generation never wanted to grow old. Just like women, they want to fend off the effects of aging as long as possible and buy themselves more time.

The biggest difference in catering to men and women is in communication. Women will talk in detail about this personal topic of cosmetic enhancement openly while men are more private. In general, men want to get in, get it done and get out without much fanfare. Just tell them the facts, be upfront, keep it simple and keep the process moving along. Men will not be doing much shopping around to multiple offices. This process can be very uncomfortable for them. Connect with them and they will schedule.

Frankly, the majority of men will most likely come in through the urging of the women in their lives. Be sure your female patients know you gladly accept and welcome male patients. Then address the male patients' main concerns which are typically money and pain.

## PAIN AND MEN

Pain and men don't mix well. Men can be more pain intolerant than your female patients. They have a stronger fight or flight reaction so they may need more anesthesia and sedation.

Do whatever you can to minimize their pain to ensure they return to you again and again. Men have a more difficult time sitting still, especially for minimally invasive procedures such as injectables and laser procedures. Use blasts, blocks, ice, and general anesthesia – anything that will give them a more pleasant experience.

# PAIN IN GENERAL

> *"I go to the best Botox injector in the world. He is so gentle, my friends and I call him the 'gentle injector'. I have yet to get a bruise and can go out immediately afterwards. I used to go to this other doctor but he was rough. It was painful and I would be bruised and swollen for days."*
>
> — Stephanie, 36 years old – Botox

The subject of pain came up often while interviewing the patients for this book. They could still feel the jabs, stings, heat and aches. The memories of discomfort from surgery, injectables, lasers and other procedures returned when asking them to recall their experiences.

The patient must have as pleasant an experience as possible before, during and after their aesthetic procedures. Details count. You do not want the patient complaining to their friends, family and colleagues about their painful experience. The more comfortable the patient is, the more likely they will return to you again and again and refer others.

Use blasts, topical creams, coolers and blocks for minimally invasive procedures and an effective local cocktail or general anesthesia for surgery. Be sure you send your patients home with post-op pain medications, treatments or topicals. Their recuperation should be uneventful. They will see you as caring and compassionate to their comfort and satisfaction.

Resource: www.GioPelle.com (personalized Gel Packs)

# PATIENT COMMENTS ABOUT DOWNTIME

Several patients mentioned their injectables and laser procedures were typically painful and led to swelling and bruising for days afterwards. However, when they compared notes with their friends, they learned it didn't have to be that way. They were then open to trying different physicians known for their painless and gentle touch with little or no swelling and/or bruising. They found it difficult, and oftentimes impossible, to go back to the "heavier-handed" physician who gave them a great result but more downtime.

Again, do everything you can to make your patient's experience a pleasant one. Patients will take pain, swelling and bruising into consideration when deciding to whom they return and refer to. Offer them post-op solutions for faster recovery and less downtime. They will appreciate it.

> Resources: www.Implantech.com (Cimeosil for scars and Gelzone wraps)
> www.GioPelle.com (Gel Packs and Camouflage Kits)

# IMAGE MARKETING

## "You never get a second chance to make a first impression."

Your patient's perception of you is your reality. Whether they think you are great or not – they're right! You determine how they see, believe in and react to you. To help them see you in the best light, pay attention to the details.

Let's face it, people are so busy today they tend to size people up in a minute, make snap judgments then base all other decisions on those judgments. Their first impression of you is very important since it will stick – good or bad. You need to do everything possible to ensure it's memorable and positive.

When we don't know someone, we look for clues revealing who and what he or she values. We look at their dress, hair, shoes, etc. The same goes for your patients. When a patient is new to you and your practice, they notice your décor, your marketing materials and all your visual clues. They also notice details about your staff such as their demeanor and dress. This includes smells such as perfume, smoke and bad breath. They take in everything they see, hear, smell, touch and taste and categorize it based on their personal preferences.

That's why the external "stuff" is so important when you are meeting patients for the first time. Help them see you as professional by your attention to detail. The prospective patient who may be "shopping" will closely scrutinize your image and professionalism. Be sure you are portraying a positive one.

## POSITIONING/DIFFERENTIATING YOURSELF FROM THE COMPETITION

It's important to define who you are so your "preferred" patients and prospective patients gravitate towards you. Since you can't be everything to everybody, you need to identify your preferred patient and cater to his or her specific likes and preferences. You also need to communicate with them in a way that allows them to bond and identify with you and your values. The object is to differentiate yourself from all others so you attract the patients you want and repel the patients you don't.

Be sure the image you are projecting is in sync with the type of patient you are seeking to attract. This is a key element in marketing. It's more important than you think – especially to those who don't already know you.

Examples of positioning and differentiating include:

- The very exclusive "Dermatologist to the Stars" who caters to the celebrities and charges three times as much as his colleagues.

- The low-priced physician who is interested in quantity and catering to the mass market.

- The best nose or breast physician, the one to whom other specialists refer their patients.

- The practice catering to the working professionals who offer evening and Saturday appointments.

- The female physician who caters only to female patients.

> *Answering the following questions will help you define your positioning:*
>
> - *Which adjectives best describe you?*
>
> - *What are your preferred patient demographics?*
>
> - *Who are your competitors?*
>
> - *Why are you different from them?*
>
> - *Why should a patient go to you versus all others?*

You may be saying to yourself, "I don't want to limit myself. I want everybody to come to me." That's fine, but it's not reality. Most likely, you attract a certain demographic and socioeconomic group. You can either embrace that group or change your positioning to attract different patients.

Being known for a certain procedure is also not limiting. You may not want people to think of you as the "breast doctor." But if you are known as the breast doctor, other non-competing physicians will refer their patients to you. Patients who have breast concerns will go to you and then stay with you for other procedures if they have a good experience. The physicians will continue referring to you for breast concerns and your patients will continue to refer their friends to you for breast as well as for other procedures.

> *Popular Books: The Art of Persuasion* by Andrew Gulledge
> *How to Make Friends and Influence People* by Dale Carnegie

# DO THE RIGHT THING FOR YOUR PATIENTS

> *"He was so upfront and honest about what he could do for me and what I could realistically expect. I really appreciated that."*
>
> — *Nancy, 52 years old - Neck Lift and Liposuction*

Patients in my survey repeatedly mentioned the words "honesty" and "integrity" when describing their physicians. My advice here is to do the right thing for your patients. Give them what they want when appropriate without overselling them. While nobody wants to be sold and consumers today are savvy and sensitive to strong sales tactics, they do want to "connect" with a physician they can talk to and trust. A physician that exudes confidence and reassures the patient they will be glad they decided to move forward with the procedure with him/her will close more procedures.

Your name and reputation are invaluable – protect them at all costs.

# YOUR PERSONALITY

### #1 Rule: Be Yourself.

I assure you, most patients would prefer the real you over a phony, disingenuous you. Most people can spot a phony a mile away and don't appreciate it. They also don't trust it. So relax, be yourself (the one in a good, open, friendly mood) and work with what you have. If you need improved social skills and better rapport-building skills, there are numerous books available.

# YOUR DRESS

## White Lab Coat, Suit/Tie, Scrubs

Those surveyed preferred the aesthetic physician wear:

61%  Preferred <u>white lab coat</u>

20%  Preferred <u>suit/tie</u>

10%  Preferred <u>scrubs</u>

9%  <u>Didn't care</u> what physician wore

Most patients preferred the doctor be in a white lab coat for their consultation. It seemed the most credible and professional to them. Scrubs reminded the patients of the seriousness of the procedure and were the least favorite attire. It is also important to mention that whatever is worn be clean, ironed and presentable. Again, if someone did not refer the patient, the physician's dress was more important as the prospective patient made judgments on who would be the right physician for him or her.

51

# YOUR OFFICE

*Those surveyed commented on how important the aesthetics of the office were:*

*78% Office aesthetics were <u>very important</u>*

*20% Office aesthetics were <u>somewhat important</u>*

*2% <u>Didn't care</u> about office aesthetics*

"The difference between a good practice and a great practice is in the details."

It is the "little stuff" that differentiates you from the others. The attention to detail is so important to your patients, especially those who are considering spending an extensive amount of time and resources with you to look their best.

A nice, clean office said to those surveyed that you take pride in your office. If you care about the details and cleanliness of your office, you would also apply the same attention to the details in your work. Your office says as much about you as a person and your attitude towards your patients as any verbal communication.

Take a very objective look at your office; or better yet, have a pair of fresh eyes you trust walk through the reception area, exam rooms and surgical suite. Have them give you their observations. What does your office say about you? Are you obsessed with cleanliness, order and aesthetics or could you care less? Have you taken the time and used resources to make your office experience a pleasant one for your patients?

> *"If the doctor is conscientious about his office, he will be conscientious about my procedure."*
>
> — *Patricia, 45 years old - Bleph and Liposuction*

Here are some helpful, cost-effective ways to set up an aesthetically pleasing atmosphere:

- Spotlessly clean and dust in corners, behind books and in cabinets and drawers.

- Rid your office of all clutter: boxes, old mail, etc.

- Update your office every three years as colors, textures and designs change.

- Give your office a fresh coat of paint with soothing colors.

- Replace old worn-out drapes and blinds.

- Replace old plants with new, updated plants in the latest pottery.

- Provide soft lighting, soothing music and aesthetically pleasing artwork.

- Invest in quality, comfortable furniture and armchairs versus couches. Most patients prefer privacy and don't want to sit together.

- Display fresh flowers throughout the practice and replace them weekly.

- Optional: Provide a self-service tea caddy with carafes of coffee and hot water, assortment of tea bags, cookies, fruit and granola bars. This is gracious hospitality and gives the anxious and harried patients something to occupy or calm themselves while they anticipate their consultation.

The objective is to treat your patients as you would any visitor in your home. It will help you build rapport now and make the rest of the patient-bonding process go smoother.

## YOUR MARKETING MATERIALS

43% surveyed said printed materials were <u>very important</u>

40% surveyed said printed materials were <u>somewhat important</u>

17% surveyed said printed materials <u>not important</u>

"His printed materials showed he was savvy, up-to-date and innovative."

— Kelly, 30 years old – Rhinoplasty

Many surveyed said they had called several offices and requested information about the practice. What they got in return was, at times, surprising. Some received procedure brochures with the physician's business card enclosed. Many received the same brochures from that specialty's society or generic manufacturer brochures. Some received a very impressive presentation folder loaded with interesting procedure and practice information. Some just got a plain envelope with the physician's business card enclosed. Some didn't get anything and were told to visit the website for more information. *

If a friend highly recommended the physician the materials were still important but not as much so. Printed materials were most important when the prospective patient did not know the physician and was not referred by anyone. The prospective patient who has nothing else to go on looks at a physician's printed materials to give them a sense of the physician, their personality, values and philosophy. They were impressed when they received a packet of information on nice paper stock that included graphics, photos and specific information about their interests. They often picked the physician who sent more paper and materials than the others.

If you are trying to grow your patient database using the Internet and advertising to reach new patients, you must follow through with solid marketing materials. Most prospective patients are probably looking at other practices. You want to stand out as quality and show you have an eye for excellence and detail in your materials as well as your aesthetic procedures. These tools give the perception of added value and are effective for increasing referrals. The most important marketing collateral to have is customized:

- Business cards

- Stationery

- #10 envelopes

- Shipping labels for large white envelopes

- Note cards to be used for birthday and thank you notes

- Gift certificates

- Appointment reminder cards

Other non-essential marketing tools to differentiate you from the others and help you stand out as a true professional would include customized: Practice brochure with your photo, philosophy and credentials

- Practice brochure with your photo, philosophy and credentials

- Quarterly practice newsletter

- Large 2-pocket folder for patient information packets

- Personalized page for each procedure

- Retail bag with your practice name and logo

*Note: Sending prospective patients to your website rather than sending them a packet of information is a double-edged sword. On one hand, you save money by not sending out expensive materials. On the other hand, it can feel like a "put off" to the caller who is told to go away and visit the website and could lead to more surfing on the Internet, possibly to your competitors' websites. I would suggest doing mystery shopping in your own community to determine what others are doing. Or, better yet, differentiate yourself by sending them a professional patient information packet.

## BRANDING/CUSTOMIZED " LOOK AND FEEL"

Developing your own personality through your materials is important to your success in attracting your preferred patients to your practice. If done right, your "look and feel" evokes emotion in the patient and tells them who you are and what you value. Be sure your materials portray you accurately.

## Your Practice Logo

Your logo is your name, graphic and tagline creating a marketable and appealing identity for your practice. Be sure it's aesthetically pleasing and creates a lasting impression. Also, be sure it fits your personality. Don't let some designer create wild colors and graphics for you if you are conservative. It won't fit with your image and your patients won't identify with it. And be sure you update your look every 3-5 years.

## Your Customized Practice Brochure

Your customized practice brochure is an important sales tool. This tool sells you and your services when you're not even there and can spread your word faster than you can on your own. Your customized practice brochure establishes a strong, positive image for you and helps build trust, credibility and familiarity with your prospective patients.

Be sure your customized practice brochure includes:

- Your warm, friendly photo
- Your areas of expertise
- Your philosophy
- Your services
- Your credentials
- Your society logos
- Any PR media exposure you've had
- Patient testimonials
- Your community involvement

Your practice brochure needs to be circulated throughout your patient base and your community to help you build word-of-mouth referrals. Be sure to send it to your existing patients urging them to share it with their friends, family and colleagues. Also send it to your prospective patients who call in or email you from the Internet. Send it to those who scheduled their first appointment with you so they feel a connection with you and show up at the scheduled time. And, you want to be sure all referring physicians, nurses, spas, salons and media have your brochure so they can use you as a resource as well as a referral source.

Your brochure can be a simple, 8x11, folded in three panels or it can be a multiple-page booklet. Be sure you have it printed on high-end, glossy or matte paper and have professionals design it.

## Your Letterhead

This is your stationery, envelopes, business cards and thank-you notes. They all need to match so use the same colors, graphics and theme you used for your brochure and website. People will then identify you with your distinctive "look and feel."

Also, have these materials printed at the same time so that colors match perfectly since print shops mix colors and you could end up with different shades of the same color.

## Your Patient Information Packet

Your information packet should be high-end, informational and different from your competitors. Be sure it includes your photo, philosophy, awards, PR reprints, policies, newsletter, upcoming event invitations, before/after photos, as well as the brochures and descriptions of the procedures the prospective patient is interested in. Add a friendly, hand-written note from you or your staff to help the new patient bond with you so they show up for their appointment.

# IV

# YOUR STAFF

79% surveyed said the staff was <u>very important</u> in their decision

18% surveyed said the staff was <u>important</u> in their decision

3% surveyed said the staff was <u>somewhat important</u> in their decision

<u>Nobody</u> said staff was not important in their decision.

## STAFF'S IMAGE

Your staff reflects you. The way they talk, dress, act, look, smell (smoke, perfume or body odor) and whether they smile are all part of your image.

Implementing a dress code helps. Have a list of "dos and don'ts" such as no face piercing, visible tattoos, revealing clothing or wild jewelry. Talk about acceptable hair and makeup levels - either too much or not enough.

You may consider lab coats or some type of uniform for your staff. It looks more professional and takes care of the inappropriate clothing challenge. Also, give them name badges and business cards to make them feel part of the team. You can also display their photos on your website.

All of these simple, inexpensive tools help your staff experience ownership and will build loyalty to you and the practice.

## CHARACTERISTICS OF GOOD STAFF

Be sure you have the right team in place. Your staff can make or break your practice. When aesthetic patients are using their own money for elective procedures, their experience with you needs to be a good one – every time. Because if it's not, they will go where they are treated better and they'll take their friends with them.

A patient will spend more time with your staff than with you. It is imperative your staff is as committed to the success of your practice as you are. They need to understand they and their patient relations skills are an important, intricate part of your practice.

The staff must be approachable, caring, friendly and compassionate to every patient, every time - on the telephone, in person, or during any other interaction with your patients – it's that important.

Your staff must understand this is a sales and marketing position more than anything else. If they balk at that or say they're not good at sales, hear them and let them move on or at least move them to a position with limited patient contact. You want staff that can rise to the challenge and use their people skills to promote you, your procedures and your products. Again, while you are practicing medicine, in reality, you are also very much in sales.

Every second you spend and every dollar you invest in setting up, marketing and promoting your practice relies on your staff's support to succeed. Efficient, enthusiastic and well-trained staff members are your most valuable practice-building tools. They are the first voice your prospective patients hear. They are the first face they see. Their patient relations skills are as important as your aesthetic skills when it comes to growing your aesthetic practice.

Please be sure you have the right staff representing you.

> *"I liked the staff as much as I liked the doctor. They made me feel so welcomed and comfortable that I bragged about them to my friends."*
>
> *— Cynthia, 43 years old - Botox and Laser*

## UNDERSTANDING STAFF NEEDS

After talking with many staff members over the years, here is list of what they want from the aesthetic practice they work for:

- Recognition

- Appreciation

- Stress-free environment

- Opportunity for growth

- Continued training on new topics

- Organized work environment

- Clear understanding of expectations

- Competitive salaries

- Incentives – financial and other

- Fun on the job

- Attractive working conditions

- Ownership in their work

- Camaraderie in their workplace

## JOB RESPONSIBILITIES

Unclear staff expectations are a common complaint. Since each office works differently, be sure you have defined individual responsibilities and job descriptions for each staff person. Take nothing for granted. Spell out what their job assignments are, and when adding to those assignments, be sure you add it to their list so it's in writing. Then go over the list at their performance reviews to reiterate exactly what their responsibilities include.

Take the time with new hires to explain and train in detail exactly what is expected of them. List the duties in detail such as:

- How to answer the telephone and take messages.

- Scripting for general questions.

- Scripting on your credentials.

- Scripting on moving a caller to an appointment.

- Office procedures.

- Busy time back up help.

- Anything else you can think of that doesn't leave things to chance and mind reading.

Be sure job duties for each position are written out clearly. Have the descriptions in a binder so nobody can ever say, "That's not my job" or "I didn't know that."

> Resource: Scripting Tools Called **Exceptional Receptionist** are available at http://www.CosmeticImageMarketing.com/scripting.php

# AESTHETIC PATIENT CARE COORDINATOR

> "I loved Denise, my doctor's patient care coordinator. She was so calm and patient and led me through a very scary process from beginning to end. I'm not sure I would have gone through with it if it wasn't for her."
>
> — Helen, 59 years old - Face Lift

An aesthetic patient care coordinator (PCC) is highly recommended. They can be a wonderful buffer between you and your patients and save you a lot of time. Working together as a team can also boost your closing ratio dramatically.

The PCC's job is to promote you and your aesthetic procedures to your patients. Their job is also to book procedures and maintain contact as well as follow up with aesthetic patients on an ongoing basis. This encourages the transition from prospect to patient and then to a happy post-procedure patient who refers other patients.

> Resource: Scripting Tools Called **Staff Scripting for Success** are available at http://www.CosmeticImageMarketing.com/scripting.php

# GOAL SETTING

Share your vision with your staff. You need their buy-in and their involvement to be successful. Working with your staff, map out a plan for reaching your goals. Get suggestions from your staff so they feel invested in helping you succeed. Set quantifiable goals together for your practice on a daily, weekly, monthly or yearly basis. Monitor those goals regularly so you know how you're doing. They must be written down, measurable and obtainable. Processes must be set up to help achieve your goals. Leave nothing to chance. Give a copy of the goals to each staff member. It's also helpful to post these goals in the lunchroom so everyone can monitor their progress. Examples of goals include:

- Grow aesthetic practice by 20% this year to $600,000

- Book 15 cosmetic surgeries per month

- See 10 new aesthetic patients per week

- Book one more face lift per month

It is also helpful and more compelling when you add "why" to each goal. This way, everyone is on the same page and understands why this is important to you AND them. Do some brainstorming with the staff. An example is:

## Goal

Grow aesthetic practice by 20% this year to $600,000.

### Why This Goal:

- More fun working with healthy patients versus sick patients.

- Less stress when working with fewer patients.

- More revenues will mean increased job security.

- More aesthetic services will mean less insurance paperwork.

### How to Achieve This Goal:

- Raise prices by 5%

- Send out quarterly practice newsletter

- Coordinate bi-monthly vendor lunch-n-learn meetings

# MOTIVATING YOUR STAFF

Keeping your staff motivated to do their very best every day is an ongoing challenge. Regular staff meetings, birthday luncheons and holiday parties are a good start but may not be enough for the long run. Here are additional ideas to keep your staff working up to their potential:

## Commission

To varying degrees, most people are financially motivated. The simplest way to get your staff to do what you want is to compensate them for a job well done and extra when they go the extra mile. Some type of profit-sharing program usually helps. It can be a simple plan paying a bonus on anything over your usual revenues. Divide the bonus evenly among staff members. This not only gives your staff an incentive to go the extra mile, it also helps them self-police the slackers, especially when you're absent. Reward them for saving money and decreasing expenses. Offer a special bonus for any great ideas they bring to you. It will keep them creative and looking out for your bottom line.

## Acknowledgement

Motivation is not just about money. One common reason employees leave jobs is because they feel management does not appreciate and acknowledge them. The remedy is easy. Be sure you compliment your staff when they do something right. Saying "Thank You" still goes a long way. It's the acknowledgement and appreciation they want as much as the compensation for doing a good job. Please don't take them for granted.

## Complimentary Services

Since your staff members should look the part when promoting cosmetic enhancement, offer them free ancillary services and products at cost. Give them a monetary break on surgical procedures including discounts, no charge or pay-over-time. You want them to be able to explain first-hand to your prospective patients their own experiences and how great they feel about their enhancement. When your staff becomes your walking/talking testimonials, your revenues can easily double and triple.

## Continuing Education

A win-win for everyone is continuing education. Courses help your staff better understand the aesthetic patient, improve their selling skills and become better employees. Continuing education energizes your staff. They will appreciate you valuing them enough to invest in them.

They will also come back from these courses with new ideas and new (or improved) attitudes. This, in turn, makes them more valuable to your practice.

For example, if your receptionist shows a great interest in skin care and wishes to play a bigger role in your practice you can send her to beauty school to get her aesthetician license. She now becomes a revenue generator for you and grows that business quickly since she already knows your patients. And, she can attract new patients to your practice with these additional services so everyone benefits.

## Promotions

Consider promoting key staff members to manage the profit and loss of their own small business unit within your practice. They will feel much more responsible when they are held accountable to the bottom line.

For instance, you can promote your laser nurse to Director of Minimally-Invasive Procedures, Treatments and Retail. Give her a percentage of sales. She will feel empowered and motivated to watch over the ordering, stocking and sales. Since she has a vested interest, she will manage the staff, her time and the patients more efficiently. She will come up with ways to sell more and utilize the staff more resourcefully.

# TRAINING YOUR STAFF

Training is the most important yet most overlooked part of an aesthetic practice. It is often assumed staff members know what to do, especially if they came from another medical practice. However, they are not trained for your specific practice.

Team success training ensures every member understands how you want your practice run. Your practice is different from every other practice and it's different because you have a unique personality and you set the tone for how you want it. Each staff member needs to know and be reminded of your image and your preferences.

Here are simple ways to train staff:

- Hold 30-minute staff meetings the same day and time each week so nobody can say they didn't know about it.

- Have a training manual and pick a staff person each week to review a section or process.

- Have a semi-annual full day staff meeting to determine where you are, where you want to be and what needs to be done to get you there.

- Schedule lunch-n-learn programs with vendors to learn about each   product and procedure you offer. It's imperative every staff member   answer general questions consistently since patients will often ask you and your staff the same questions.

- Have every staff member read this book and then meet once a week to discuss it chapter-by-chapter.

## CROSS TRAINING

All new staff should start at the reception desk for one or two weeks and answer telephones along with the receptionist. This will help them understand your patients, their typical questions, your processes, how to schedule appointments, etc. It's important you have an employee binder at each telephone including all necessary information. Telephone calls on your credentials and frequently asked questions (FAQs) on each procedure are common and answers should be readily available.

Not only are the telephones one of the most important aspects of your practice, the staff needs to understand just how important every call is. The staff can impact that call – good or bad. Every staff member needs to be able to answer the telephone, answer questions and move the caller to schedule an appointment. A ringing telephone must be answered - no matter whose job it is.

Be sure you have a plan in place to address busy times. Have the back office staff be prepared and trained on how to check patients in and out, schedule appointments, process payments and so on.

> *Resource: Staff Scripting Tools are available at:*
>
> *http://www.CosmeticImageMarketing.com/scripting.php*

## MANAGING STAFF

You really don't want to manage your staff. That takes too much time and effort. Instead, your staff should care about your practice. Determine obtainable goals. Encourage them to manage themselves to achieve those goals. Map out processes so everyone on your team knows what to do and when.

Frankly, most physicians don't have the interest, skills or time to manage properly. I recommend hiring an experienced office manager with excellent people and management skills. The manager can monitor everyone's productivity and training. You can then concentrate on what you do best. You also want them to be the "bad guy" when it comes to reprimanding and critiquing (criticizing) a staff person's work. Your staff needs to "sell" you affectionately to the patients. If you just reprimanded them for something, they are not as likely to eagerly sing your praises. Let your office manager handle those challenges of managing your practice. And, be sure to give your office manager the executive authority to reprimand and even fire employees so the staff will take them seriously.

By the way, your office manager must be able to gently manage you as well, without fear of reprisal. When the manager sees something you could improve upon, i.e., making patients wait or saying something inappropriate in front of a patient, they should be able to discuss it with you.

## WHERE TO FIND GOOD STAFF

Hire personality and a great winning attitude and then train for competence. It's much easier to train someone to do the job. It's much more difficult (impossible) to change their personality. Go with the employee who naturally is nice, pleasant, friendly, easy-going, eager to learn and well liked by the other staff members. Experience is nice but can sometimes be a hindrance when training employees for your particular preferences. Always be on the lookout for new employees from the following sources:

- Patients or their friends and family members
- Hospital staff looking for a change
- Aestheticians in your community
- Sales people at makeup counters at department stores
- Other medical offices
- Vendors or their family and friends

71

- Anyone from service-oriented businesses such as Nordstrom or high-end hotels

- Employment agencies (fee)

- Websites such as www.Craigslist.org or www.Monster.com (fee)

Staffing is the most challenging yet important aspects of your practice. It will take ongoing time and effort to find and keep the best people.

# AESTHETIC SALES 101 SKILLS FOR STAFF

If you like your staff but know they are reluctant to "sell" give them an opportunity to shift their perceptions. Keep it simple. Rather than use the term "sell" which automatically repels some, try using the word "promote". Offer them some type of incentive (monetary or otherwise) to help them get over that hump and improve their attitude about becoming more assertive. And, give them the following training and tools they need to help you promote your services:

## Rapport-Building Skills

They should treat every single patient, every single time, the same as they would a good friend visiting them. When a patient first opens the door to your practice, the staff should be there to acknowledge, greet, smile, say hello and use the patient's name so they feel welcomed and special.

## Verbal Cheerleading

A few words of encouragement can help the patient make a decision and also feel good about their purchase. Script your staff to say the following when appropriate and ask them to come up with more key phrases like:

> *"Sara, you are going to love Botox. We've all had it and can't live without it."*

> *"Heather, you might be bruised now but you are going to look fantastic in no time."*

> *"Cynthia, this skin care line is going to have your skin glowing in less than a month."*

## Selling the Physician

Your staff's primary job is to promote you, your credentials and your services to your patients. Be sure they know how wonderful you are and everything about you and your accomplishments so they can relay that to your patients and prospective patients. Again, it's helpful if you have performed procedures and treatments on your staff so they can relay their first-hand experiences to your patients.

## Closing Appointments

Staff should always attempt to book the next appointment while the patient is still in the office by saying,

> *"Sara, let's go ahead and book your next appointment now so you get the day and time you want. And, I'll be sure to call to remind you."*

73

## "Add-On" at Checkout

Staff can easily increase the order size if they simply mention any special promotions you have going now or new procedures you have added to your practice. An example is:

> *"Sara, just so you know, we have a special Internet offer this month that gives you a free IPL treatment with your purchase of Botox and filler. If you're interested, you would save $500."*

---

*Resource:*

*Staff Scripting Tools are available at:*
*http://www.CosmeticImageMarketing.com/scripting.php*

---

# YOUR EXTERNAL IMAGE

These are the tools you present on a wide scale for everyone to see. Your external image is very important in attracting your preferred patient and detracting others. Be sure to include the right messaging and "look and feel" in these image-building tools. These prospective patients don't know you. They will be looking for clues as to who you are and what you value.

## Your Website

> "Her website was amazing. It was pretty and had lots of information on it with pictures. It also had a video of her, her staff and office so I felt comfortable visiting her. She also answered an email I sent her and that was cool."
>
> — Stacey, 25 years old - Breast Aug

It is mandatory you have a website. Your website is your business card of today and it must be informative, interesting and quick and easy to navigate. It's your public relations tool and establishes you as a plausible practice and a valuable resource. Additionally, it gives you credibility and helps the patient get to know you before meeting. It can also help you maintain relationships with your current patients and grow your practice by adding referral tools.

Your website should include:

- Aesthetically pleasing home page with limited flash so it's quick to download.

- Easy navigation bar so patients can go directly to their interests.

- Nice graphics offering a theme throughout the website.

- Invitation to enter email address for e-newsletters or exclusive web offers.

- "Send this to a friend" link.

- Introduction about you, your philosophy and values.

- Photographs of you, your staff, your reception area, your exam rooms and tasteful photos of your surgical suite (nothing graphic to scare them.)

- Many before/after patient photos since prospective patients want to see your work.

- Description of each procedure and treatment.

- Patient Testimonials and stories in writing and on video.

Your website should be unique, functional and one of quality. You need to decide if your website is an informational brochure your current and prospective patients can use to learn more about you and your practice or if it's an interactive sales tool to attract new patients. Costs vary dramatically depending on your intent, how detailed you want it to be and who designs it. You may know of a website designer who understands the technology well but not the aesthetic industry. Or you may know someone who understands the aesthetic industry but not the technnical world of Internet marketing. You want a blend of both to make the best use of your website. Do not skimp in this area by using your teenage nephew who is taking a computer course in school. He will not have the expertise or the industry know-how to understand your target market and what attracts them to your practice. Use professionals who can design the right look and feel for you.

Resources: www.MedNet-Tech.com

www.EtnaInteractive.com

## Tracking Website Traffic

It is important you know where your Internet leads are coming from so you know where to invest in your own Website's search engine optimization as well as the vendor portals and Web directories. You also want to track your internal processes to follow up on Internet leads to ensure the inquirer gets a prompt response when they contact you and your staff for additional information.

Resource: www.MyMedLeads.com

## On-Line Patient Education

Patients are looking for information about procedures. Adding detailed information about the procedure, expected results, risks, etc. to your website helps attract and keep prospective patients on your website longer. It also increases the conversion rate to an appointment and saves you time during the consultation.

> Resource: wwwUnderstand.com

## Search Engine Optimization (SEO)

With the explosive growth of the Internet, it's getting more difficult to be found on the Internet by happenstance. Your prospective patients are going to search engines such as Yahoo or Google to type in key words of interest. Thousands of website results come up and that makes it extremely difficult to get exposure.

SEO selects and monitors key words and phrases to help you get the best and highest positioning on the Internet. However, it's not for amateurs. Although it can cost you thousands of dollars to hire professionals to handle and monitor this for you, it can be money well spent if your goal is to attract new patients from the Internet.

Getting exposure on the Internet requires an entire education on its own and can be complex. If you are trying to bring in prospective patients from the Internet, pay for the professionals to handle it for you.

Otherwise, just be sure you have your website address (URL) on every single piece of communication that goes out of your office. That way, your patients can refer their friends, family and colleagues to your website and they themselves will visit from time to time to see what's new.

Be sure your web address is on your:

- Practice brochure
- Letterhead and business card
- Envelopes and shipping labels
- On-hold message
- Direct mail pieces
- Power point slides
- Ads
- Product labels

> *Resources: www.MedNet-Tech.com*
> *www.EtnaInteractive.com*

## Vendor Portals and Directories

Another way to be found on the Internet is through someone else's website. Rather than spending your own time, money and resources on search engine optimization, you pay a smaller fee to a vendor who already has traffic visiting their website and good positioning with the search engines.

> *Resources: www.BotoxCosmetic.com*
> *www.CosmeticSurgery.com*
> *www.Juvederm.com*
> *www.RestylaneUSA.com*
> *www.YourPlasticSurgeryGuide.com*

## Your External Advertising

If you promote your services through mass media advertising in newspapers, local radio/TV and cable TV, be sure the message and image portray you accurately. Use professionals to be sure the communication is getting to and connecting with your preferred patient. Monitor its success to determine if you are getting a good return on your investment.

> *Resource: www.BurkeMarketing.net*

# VI

# OFFICE PROCEDURES AND PATIENT RELATIONS

Every encounter with the aesthetic patient is an important one. That means it's important every patient have a great experience with you every time, whether on the telephone or in person.

## WHY AESTHETIC PATIENTS LEAVE A PRACTICE

The survey indicated patients leave a practice for the following reasons:

- Impersonal service

- Rude or dismissive staff

- Poorly-trained staff

- Unprofessional image

- Condescending physician

- Felt oversold

- Felt they received less than promised

- Felt disrespected

- Long waiting times

- Misunderstandings regarding payment

- Too expensive

- Didn't get prompt return call

- Staff was too busy

- Too many confusing telephone options

- The telephone was not picked up in a timely fashion

# IMPORTANCE OF TELEPHONES

*"I called around to a couple of offices and was surprised how unhelpful one was and how rude another one was when I was abruptly placed on hold. The third office I called was friendly and answered all of my questions so I booked with them."*

— *Kelly, 28 years old – Laser Hair Removal*

The average aesthetic practice loses more than 100 telephone inquiries every year because they either don't answer the telephone promptly, or at all, or someone answers rudely or with disinterest.

A ringing telephone represents an opportunity. The telephone is a powerful marketing tool in your practice. If the call is handled correctly, it's the first of many calls to your practice. If not handled correctly, it's the first and last call to your practice. You lose not only that caller but also their referrals to their friends, family and colleagues.

Properly used, the telephone and receptionist are vital to your marketing efforts in prospecting, reactivating and handling everyday routine processes for patient communications and service.

> *Please answer the telephone immediately, politely and knowledgeably!*

# IMPORTANT ROLE OF THE RECEPTIONIST

The receptionist is the most pivotal person in your practice. The person answering your telephone is the *"voice"* of your practice and has the power to begin, or end, a relationship with a prospective patient. Keep in mind your skills are secondary if your receptionist doesn't have the right communication skills to get the prospective patient in to meet you.

Each time the telephone rings, that call represents not only an initial sale in the amount of your average order size but also several sales after that from that returning patient as well as their referred friends, family and colleagues.

A patient relationship begins before the caller even becomes a patient. If someone calls and bonds with your receptionist, then you will have fewer no-shows, increased conversions from calls to appointments and a more receptive prospective patient during your consultation.

It is critical to your success that you have the right person answering the telephone. They must possess the following:

- A pleasant voice

- A positive attitude

- A friendly and helpful nature

- A genuine interest/concern for people

- Enthusiasm when speaking to callers

- They address people by name

- They talk *to* people, not *at* them

- They use their manners

- They apologize when a caller is put on hold

- They concentrate on this call, not the one before or after and give their full, undivided attention

- They establish and maintain rapport

- They listen actively by acknowledging what they are hearing from the caller and repeating it back to them to be sure they understood correctly

- They enunciate and are articulate

- They vary their tone and pitch so it doesn't sound like they're reading or they are bored

- They wait for an answer to key questions and they allow time for the caller to think and respond

- When they are interrupted, they politely answer the question and then get back on script

- If there's a problem, they listen to the entire problem without interrupting and then offer solutions

Your receptionist must be set up to win. Be sure the receptionist has the time to spend on the telephone and this is not just one of many of her* duties. She must not view the telephone as an annoyance but rather as an opportunity. Everybody in the office must understand the importance of this position and support the receptionist.

*Note: I suggest using a female receptionist if you are attempting to attract female patients to your aesthetic practice. My research has shown a female will bond more easily with another female answering the telephone.

# SCRIPTING

Half the battle is promptly answering the telephone and the other half is actually being helpful to the caller. The receptionist must be equipped with information to keep the call moving along to the next step.

> *Resource:*
>
> *Scripting Tools Called* **Exceptional Receptionist** *is available at*
> *http://www.CosmeticImageMarketing.com/scripting.php*

# AESTHETIC SALES 101 SKILLS FOR THE RECEPTIONIST

The following steps include tips to help your receptionist convert more callers to appointments.

## The Opening: Initial Telephone Inquiry

When answering the telephone, your only goal is to convert this telephone inquiry into an appointment. You just want to convince the caller to meet the doctor. You have 20 seconds to peak the caller's interest. Use an upbeat, friendly voice and inflection to get the ball rolling.

The best way to bond with a caller is to share information. Start with offering your name to then get their name:

> Receptionist: *"Good afternoon, Dr. Jones' office, Catherine speaking. How may I help you?"*
>
> Caller: *"Hi Catherine, this is Sally and I'm interested in learning more about Botox."*
>
> Receptionist: *"Hi, Sally. I can help you with that."*

It is then crucial you now learn how they heard about the practice. So, simply ask them in a conversational tone:

> Receptionist: *"By the way Sally, how did you hear about Dr. Jones?"*

Enter that information on a telephone tracking form next to you or in the computer. It will help you understand how prospective patients are learning about the practice.

---

*Download a free telephone tracking form from www.CosmeticImageMarketing.com/phonelog*

---

## Qualifying the Caller

This is a double-edged sword. You want to close every caller for an appointment but you may be finding there are too many "shoppers" clogging your practice. They are casually visiting several offices and not yet sure when or if they will book. To cut down on the number of "lookey-loos" in the practice, it's helpful to ask qualifying questions such as:

- What is the caller's main concern?

- When did they want to do something about it?

- How did they hear about you? If it's a friend, close them! If it's the newspaper or Internet find out if they're shopping around and what their criteria is for choosing a physician (price, location, etc.)

However, you don't want to over-qualify and lose the caller because of aggressive sales techniques. Develop a relationship over the telephone and they'll often tell you a lot and be anxious to meet you in person.

Also, avoid conducting a telephone consultation. The more information provided over the telephone, the less likely the caller will come to your office. You need to strike a balance between providing a concise, positive answer indicating your knowledge and confidence and providing too much information. However, callers want their questions answered quickly. Answer now, but if you can't, promise to call them back within a day and then call them within one hour. It's always better to under-promise and over-deliver.

## Converting Caller to Appointment

Ask for the appointment and then promise you will call to remind them of their appointment.

Give the caller alternatives so they decide on a choice rather than yes or no on the appointment:

> *"These are all great questions Sally and I know Dr. Smith would like to answer them for you personally. He would need to see you to address your specific skin type, tone and condition. Let's schedule a time for you to speak with him. Actually, he has an opening this Friday at 1pm or would you prefer next Tuesday morning at 10?"*

If you can't convert them, here is a nice way to obtain the prospective patient's contact information so you can follow-up:

> *"Well Sally, it sounds like you're not ready to book a consultation just yet so let me send you some information about Dr. Smith and this procedure so you have it handy when you are ready. May I get your mailing address please?"*

Then, send them a "thank you for calling" letter written on the practice letterhead. Add a handwritten comment to personalize it. Enclose the letter with a practice brochure as well as information about the procedure they are interested in. Follow up with a telephone call several days later. After speaking with you and reading your materials, they may feel more comfortable booking an appointment.

## Sell Your Physician

Be knowledgeable about your physician's credentials and what sets him/her apart from your competitors. It's important to state any board certifications, special training, awards and expertise in the procedure the caller is interested in. List all of the above on a cheat sheet and have it available near each telephone for easy access.

## Handling Objections

If the patient is not ready to set an appointment with your urging, that means they do not yet see the value of the consultation. Although you will not always get an appointment on the first call, your scripting should help increase the closing ratios. If they give you objections, follow these guidelines:

1) Hear them out so you understand their concerns.

2) Tell them you understand.

3) Answer their concerns with pre-scripted responses and include anecdotal information about the experiences of other patients who felt the same way. Ask again for the consultation.

If they are still not sure, offer them something – an invitation to your next seminar, your quarterly newsletter or this month's special email offer for patients only (but you'll make an exception.)

## Pricing Questions

You want to avoid stating prices over the telephone if you can. However, in today's reality, patients are demanding and want to know. They may just move on to the next practice if they feel like they are struggling to get information out of you.

Before quoting price ranges be sure to reiterate your physician's credentials to help explain why he/she may be more expensive than the competitors.

Tell callers about value-added benefits your practice offers such as the fact that your brand new surgical suite offers privacy and comfort, that your special nursing staff is available to take them home, or that you offer a block for painless injectables and take-home ice packs for them to keep, etc.

You also want to state big price ranges since it's impossible to quote exact pricing without first examining the patient. Break prices down to the minimal and separate them if they are surgical – one for the doctor, one for the anesthesia and one for the OR time. Again, tell them the physician's credentials and other fine points differentiating you from the competitors. Be sure to mention you offer financing options as well. Some examples:

> *"We are affordable and competitive with the other "top" physicians in the area."*

> *"It will cost anywhere from $3,000 to $5,000 or we offer easy monthly payments starting at $50/month."*

> *"We try to keep our pricing affordable for everyone by offering monthly payment plans. So, starting at $50/month, you can have what you want now rather than wait any longer."*

> *"We are not the cheapest or the most expensive, but I am confident we will give you a great result."*

---

*Resource: www.CareCredit.com*

---

## Closing Appointment

Here are some closing statements to move the caller to an appointment:

- *"So Sally, did you have a particular day in mind that you wanted to visit?"*

- *"Thanks for calling …. well, the doctor is available on (two dates and times) Do either of those work for you?"*

- *"Your own personal evaluation is the best place to start. That way, you can have all of your individual questions answered. You can see our facility, meet Dr. Smith and our staff and talk to other patients as well. Let's go ahead and schedule a date and time for you to come in and see us. Do you prefer morning or afternoon?"*

- Sell scarcity. Give the caller the impression your physician is extremely busy:

  *"Dr. Smith is heavily booked this month but let see me where I can fit you in."*

# ON-HOLD MESSAGING

Placing a caller on hold is unavoidable so make it as pleasant as possible. Be sure you have an informative message that outlines your services, informs callers of new procedures, invites callers to events and educates them on your credentials. Not only will this distract them from being on hold, they may hear about something they want to learn more about and may schedule a consultation without much prompting.

*Resource: www.WaitMediaGroup.com*

# ANSWERING SERVICE/TELEPHONE FEATURES

Telephones must be answered by a human voice during normal business hours, even during lunch hour. Again, aesthetic patients are more demanding and may only have time to call during their lunch hour. They need to be accommodated or you'll lose them.

If you cannot answer the telephone by the third ring, have an answering machine pick up with your receptionist's friendly voice. The callers will most likely appreciate a message like this:

> *"Hello. This is Susan at Dr. Smith's office. I'm sorry I'm not available for you, but your call is very important to me so please hold or leave a message with your name and telephone number. I will return your call momentarily. Thank you for calling and I'll speak with you soon."*

Invest in a good telephone system and place telephones throughout your office so they can be picked up promptly by anyone. Be sure they include the feature that beeps every 20 seconds to remind you someone is on hold.

Another nice telephone feature includes a system with sounds other than ringing since that can be stressful for everyone listening. Cordless headsets are also helpful for multi-tasking as well as long, retractable or wireless telephones for efficiency and ease.

# ANSWERING EXCHANGES

Services are available to answer the telephone for you when you're not available but choose wisely. Mystery-shop several exchanges to determine the quality and service of each. You want to ensure they pick up the telephone by the third ring and they answer the telephone with enthusiasm and interest just as your own receptionist would. This answering service exchange is part of your image. It needs to reflect you and your values. Be sure it is representing you positively.

# TRACKING TELEPHONE RESULTS

It is imperative that you track incoming telephone calls. This quantifiable data will tell you so much. It will help you determine what promotional efforts are working, what your patients are most interested in learning more about and what your conversion rates are. You should be able to track:

- How many calls you get.

- Of those calls, how many are current patients or prospective patients?

- If prospective patient – how did they hear about you?

- If current patient – what prompted them to call?

- Who and how many are calling because of a special promotion such as your newsletter, advertisement, etc?

- Of those calling, how many booked a consultation?

- Of the booked consultations, how many booked a treatment and/or bought products?

- Of those who booked procedures, what were the revenues generated?

If any of your conversion rates are abnormally low, you must determine why. Perhaps your staff needs more training and/or perhaps you need more staff. You need to find out!

Regarding marketing efforts, the return on your investment (ROI) can only be calculated based on accurate tracking - starting with the initial telephone inquiry. Be sure your staff understands the importance of tracking since some will have a resistance to this and view it as extra work.

Consider setting up a separate line specifically for any of your outside marketing and advertising efforts so you don't even need to ask the callers where they heard about you. And, if you are expecting many calls that could interrupt your normal office flow, you can hire an outside call center to take those calls and bypass your office altogether.

> Download a free telephone tracking form at
> http://www.CosmeticImageMarketing.com/phonelog

## MYSTERY SHOP

If you were to call your own practice today would you schedule an appointment? Would you be treated well on the telephone and want to book a consultation to learn more about you and your practice?

To find out, mystery shop your office using your neighbors and friends to be sure your telephone is being answered and questions are being handled properly. You can spend thousands of dollars on marketing and advertising but if your staff cannot convert the telephone calls into consultations then your dollars are wasted.

# PATIENT RELATIONSHIP SOFTWARE PROGRAM

A good patient-relations software program is a must. You have to be able to create an entire story and history about a patient at a push of a button. It's vital to know:

- your patients' buying habits

- if they attended your events

- if they responded to your mailings

- if they referred friends, family and colleagues

- their children's names

- their occupation, etc.

- their email address

- their birth month, etc.

You are building a relationship with this patient and knowledge is power. Patients are always impressed when you remember their birthday or something about their family. You don't have to remember if you enter it into the software program and refer back to it periodically. When you automate your entire process, it becomes pre-programmed so you are less likely to lose that patient because of a lack of patient relations.

The reporting feature of your software program is vital and should be able to give you very detailed reports on every aspect of your practice such as:

- Referral reports in detail.

- Segmented patient lists by age, geography, birthday months and other demographics.

- Segmented patient lists by purchases; i.e., Botox patients, wrinkle filler patients, etc.

- Revenue streams by product, procedure and treatments.

- Comparable revenues for same periods for different years.

- Specific ROI results per marketing or advertising effort.

Your software program is the "hub" of your practice. Be sure you have the right one in place to help you monitor, maintain and grow your aesthetic practice.

---

*Resource: www.WaitMediaGroup.com*

---

## CONSULTATION FEE

The age-old question is whether to charge for a consultation or not. That's a good question and the answer is yes and no.

Your time is valuable and should be compensated. You are not in the business of just meeting people. You are in the business of treating patients. However, with the competition heating up and more advertising offering complimentary consultations, many aesthetic patients today would not dream of paying for a consultation, especially if they are shopping around and found you through mass marketing efforts such as the Internet or newspaper.

It also depends on your preferred target market. If you are going for the higher-end clientele and higher-ticket prices, charge a hefty consultation fee. It will distinguish you as a true professional. If you are going after the mass market and lower ticket items, then it's probably best to offer a free* consultation; however, you need to close them once they are in the door.

For everyone else, I would say charge a consultation fee but use it as a special offer if they attend your seminar or open house. That way, they did something to receive something free. This has perceived value.

*I use the word "free" versus "complimentary" consultation on purpose. Patients respond to free more than to complimentary.

## NO-SHOWS

Patients not showing up for scheduled appointments are just a fact of life in the aesthetic world. Because these patients are not sick, there's a better chance they will change their mind and not keep their appointment. To keep this to a minimum, it's important to build that relationship with the patient from the start. When they call, have your receptionist use their name and collect as much personal information as they can. Have your staff send a patient information packet with a "Welcome to Our Practice" letter. Jot down a personal, handwritten note saying you look forward to meeting the prospective patient. Be sure they call the patient 48 hours ahead of time to remind them of their appointment, and use email reminders as a back-up.

If they do not show for their appointment, wait 20 minutes and have your staff call them. There is a chance they simply forgot, they are lost, they are running late or they had an emergency. This concern on your part will keep the relationship going and your staff may be able to reschedule them. Keep it friendly and conversational so they are not embarrassed to reschedule. They may appreciate your understanding. If your staff cannot reschedule, offer to send them your quarterly newsletter, periodic specials and upcoming event notices. Perhaps the timing is just not right for them so they are not saying "no"; they are just saying "not now" or "not yet". When they are ready to revisit their aesthetic concerns, your name should pop into their head since you have been communicating with them on a consistent and friendly basis.

Resource: www.SmileReminder.com

## NO-SHOW POLICY

I suggest implementing a no-show policy to reduce your wasted time and opportunity costs. State your policy in the initial telephone call with the prospective patient so they understand they will be charged if they don't cancel within 24 hours. Display your policy at the checkout counter as well. You may even want to get a credit card number up front so the aesthetic patient understands you take this very seriously. Even if you never enforce it, just informing your patients of your no-show policy helps.

# THE PATIENT EXPERIENCE

The sign of a truly professional office is when the patient experience is so smooth and effortless the patient enjoyed visiting you. They leave happy and satisfied. The aesthetic patient needs to feel the practice is serene, efficient and organized and the staff knows what they are doing. This will help them decide positively on procedures and surgery and stay with you for years to come. If your practice is hectic, busy and scattered, your patients will feel that and be less inclined to return for more.

## The Initial Visit to Your Office

A new patient will most likely be feeling some anxiety if they don't know you. Make it as easy and comfortable as possible for them at every step in the process. Be sure the new patient knows exactly how to get to your office. If it's tricky – help them on the telephone when they are scheduling their first appointment. Be sure to give directions, tips for parking and any helpful information about floors, hallways or signs they should look for.

Once in your office, be sure the patient experience is a good one. Decide ahead of time how the patient will move through your office and through the various stages of an office visit with you.

## Greeting the Patient

Make the patient feel welcomed and comfortable just as you would when your friends visit your home. Welcome them with a smile; offer them a seat, refreshments and small talk. Play soothing music and provide a relaxing atmosphere. All of these efforts will have a huge positive impact on the harried and nervous aesthetic patient.

## Reception Area

This is your "reception area" and never the "waiting room." You don't want to remind them they are waiting since they will feel disrespected if kept waiting too long. However, if they are waiting for you, use that time to:

- <u>Educate</u> using your practice brochure, procedure brochures, "ask-me about" tools and anything else to help explain each procedure, treatment and product you offer.

- <u>Distract</u> with your beautiful before/after photo books, testimonial book and a video introducing them to you, your practice, procedures, testimonials, etc.

- <u>Entertain</u> with great magazines like People, Business Week and Oprah, a telephone for local calling and perhaps a computer with an Internet connection.

> Resource: www.Understand.com
> www.WaitMediaGroup.com

## Waiting

Do not make your patients wait! It is disrespectful and implies your time is more valuable than theirs. This is the number one complaint with those surveyed and should not be taken lightly. The aesthetic patient is a consumer. They are spending their own money and expect service. They know they have options. The impression the aesthetic patient should receive is you and your staff eagerly awaiting their arrival and making time in your busy schedule to give them the service they require – especially if they are considering invasive procedures.

In general, the aesthetic patient has about a 20-minute threshold for waiting. After that, you'd better entertain and distract that patient or they may walk out and never come back. If you are delayed, tell the staff so they can tell the patients in order to update them. Have your staff go to the reception area and explain the delay.

The best way to ensure a smooth-flowing schedule is to book blocks of unhurried time to allow for complete consultations. This also eliminates the prospective patient sitting next to or even seeing the post-op patient who is not fully healed and may not yet be ecstatic with their results. Seeing a post-op patient reminds them of the unpleasant side of cosmetic enhancement and you don't need that patient relaying negative anecdotal information about their discomfort or pain.

Also, book minimally invasive procedures in blocks of time but don't double or triple book. Stay on schedule. If a patient asks for more treatments than originally scheduled, try to accommodate them only if it does not interfere with the rest of your schedule. If it does, invite them back when you have more time.

> *Waiting can hurt every other step in your process.*
>
> *Please stay on top of it.*

## Paperwork

Hand the patient a confidential fold-over clipboard folder with the in-take paperwork and a high-quality pen printed with your practice name and then let them keep the pen. Do not yell their name from across the room. Go to them quietly to preserve their privacy and hand them the necessary portfolio of paperwork. If it's an existing patient, be sure you have pulled their chart and have any additional paperwork ready for them.

When they return the paperwork to you, be sure they have filled in the referral box since you must know how they heard about you. If they haven't, in a very conversational tone, ask, *"So Jean, how did you hear about us?"* and note it on the form.

Also, if they have not filled in their email address, again in a conversational tone, say,

> *"Just to let you know, Jean, we offer very exclusive web offers throughout the year so if you provide your email address, I'll be sure you get them."*

More often than not the patients want your special offers, so ask!

## Escort Patient into the Office

It is important for a staff member to escort a patient from room to room and introduce them to the next person they will encounter. Although it is best if the patient sits still and the staff moves around, if that's not possible, make it as effortless as possible so they don't feel "herded."

## Pre-Meeting with Staff

The patient care coordinator should spend a considerable amount of time with the patient so she understands the patient's particular concerns. Provide computer imaging and/or skin analysis sessions and educate the patient about the details of the procedure, treatment or surgery and expected results, recovery, post-op care, etc. This time spent together is crucial in developing a relationship with the patient and helps the patient develop a bond with the staff, thus, the practice. This is also a good time for the patient care coordinator to brag about you and what makes you the most logical choice.

The objective here is to bond with the patient and have them feel like they are in good hands and happy to be there. You know your staff has bonded when the patient tells them exactly what their intent is such as they are just looking, they have an event coming up; they just had a windfall - whatever. The patient may be more likely to open up to your patient care coordinator than with you if your authority intimidates them. Be sure you have the right person in place for that position.

## Exam

While the patient is preparing for you to come in, staff should be prepping you on everything they know about this patient. Then you know the type of approach to take, the patient's financial and emotional situation and how much time to spend with them.

Be sure you knock and wait for an answer before you enter the exam room. It's polite and might avoid an embarrassing moment. Staff can enter the room with you and say,

*"Dr. Smith, this is Anne. Anne's daughter is getting married in six months and she wants to look her best for the big occasion."*

## Closing Techniques

The Choice: Always give the patient a choice of one or the other rather than yes or no. Remember: you are not pressuring the patient to book; you are simply offering your services and the next logical step. Keep it conversational:

*"Sally, would you like to take advantage of the multiple treatment package to save yourself $300 or buy just one treatment today?"*

*"We are very booked so let me give you some of the earliest dates we have available. How about next Tuesday at 10 am or would next Friday at 3 pm be more convenient for you?"*

*"Let's look at some surgery dates. Do you have a specific day in mind or shall I tell you what our earliest possibilities are?"*

## Handling Objections

The same objections will come up 90% of the time. Be prepared ahead of time to address them with skillfully thought-out responses that sound reasonable and professional.

Use emotions when confronted with objections. Remember: objections are a good thing. Objections mean that a patient is seriously considering a treatment and may need some prodding to help get them to that final decision. Here are some examples:

**Fear of pain and surgery:**
**Fear- Felt- Found Method:**

- *"Sally, it's normal to feel that way."*

- *"Others have also felt the exact same way you have,"* (Reassure the patient it's a normal response)

- *"And, what they found was that it was much easier than they thought and they wish they had done it years ago since they now feel so much better about themselves."*

**Money:**

Emotional Appeal:

> *"Mike, you said this has bothered you for years and you would feel so much better about yourself if you had it fixed. What is that worth to you for the next 10 years? A better love life, more confidence, better job, etc.?"*

**Deciding:**

Emotional/Practical:

> *"Heather, you can decide now to make things better or you can wait. What happens if you wait another year? Will it get better or worse? Will you be happier that you didn't do anything or happier that you did something about what's bothering you?"*

If you have taken the time to bond with your prospective patient, reassured them they are in good hands and you have shown results with photos and testimonials, deciding when they want to have something done should be the next logical step. If the patient is not ready to book surgery or a procedure, a personalized follow-up letter needs to go out with a hand-written personal note on it from the patient care coordinator. The note should mention something personal between the two of them to continually build that relationship.

Also, offer to follow up with event invitations, exclusive web offers and other marketing efforts. This will keep your name in front of them when they are ready to move forward. You never know if an aesthetic patient who is not ready today will be ready weeks, months or years from now.

## Check-Out

Be easy to do business with. Accept all credit cards and personal checks as well as cash. Make it simple for your patients to pay you any way they can.

Also, have retail products and gift certificates on display at your check-out counter. Take advantage of this opportunity to add additional items to a patient's order as long as their wallet is already out.

## Book Appointments Now

Never let a patient leave your practice without booking another appointment. The patient who says, "I'll call you" may have good intentions to do just that; however, life can get in the way and block the patient from doing so. Make every attempt to book the next appointment while they are physically in front of you. Reassure them you will call to remind them of their appointment and they can always reschedule if a conflict comes up.

If the patient is hesitant to book because she doesn't have her calendar with her, here's an effective response to use:

*"Sara, you know how busy we get here so let's do this. I'll book your next appointment 4 months from now for the same day and time as today and you can always call me to change it if you need to."*

If a patient bought a series of treatments, book them all at one time rather than one at a time in the future. They will feel more committed to your practice and keep the appointments they have set up so far in advance (just like they do at the dentist). Give them the dates in writing so they can write them into their schedule and assure them they will be reminded of their appointments as they approach. Booking a series also ensures they get the best result possible. You do not want them to complete only two treatments when they needed five and then tell their friends and family they didn't get a good result.

## Financing

Be sure your staff is prepared to offer financing on the spot so as not to hold up the decision. Several companies specialize in cosmetic financing and can give you an answer within minutes. Plant the seed early and start the paperwork process while the patient is being examined. A simple placard that says "Ask Me about Cosmetic Financing" should be conveniently displayed where the patient can see it in case they want to open up that discussion so you don't have to. You can then have a ready answer when it's time to book the procedure.

---

*Resource: www.CareCredit.com*

---

# THE PHYSICIAN'S CONSULTATION WITH THE AESTHETIC PATIENT

*"My doctor made me comfortable with her as a person first before she jumped into the medical stuff."*

*"He addressed my specific concerns and I appreciated that."*

*"He kept telling me what I wanted instead of listening to what I really wanted."*

*"I was so impressed the busy doctor spent so much time with me. It showed me he was thorough and cared about me."*

*"The doctor was so clinical and technical, he lost me early on."*

— *Various Comments from Surveys*

Your patients look to you for solutions to their problems! Listen to their concerns, show them you have a solution and can help them solve their problem. Here are basic steps to help you through a more effective process when you consult with your aesthetic patients:

## Step 1: Introduction

Have your staff prep you with the patient's particulars they learned already such as the patient's wants and psychological, emotional and financial eligibility so you know how to approach them.

Knock on the door gently before opening and greet the patient by name. Introduce yourself while you look them in the eye, smile and shake their hand.

## Step 2: Build Rapport

When those surveyed were asked why they chose the particular physician they did, the same words and phrases kept coming up:

- *"I felt so comfortable with the doctor."*

- *"He really listened to me."*

- *"She answered all my questions patiently."*

- *"There was no pressure so I felt relaxed."*

- *"He understood what I wanted."*

Women especially use their intuition to make decisions. Be sure your patients feel cared for and special. You want them to know you have compassion for them and understand their needs. You can do that by building rapport with each patient.

## What is Rapport?

Rapport is that special bond you build with your patient that creates trust and loyalty. It's that connection you make with the patient so they feel special and understood. It's also the single most important skill you can develop to be successful in this industry and to rise above your competition.

You build rapport by using touch, commonalities and mirroring.

## Touch

Physical touch builds a connection with the patient. Shake hands with your patients, touch appropriately while you examine them and touch them on the shoulder on the way out so they feel that physical connection with you.

## Commonalities

Person First – Patient Second!

You want to create and discover things you have in common with the patient. Spend a minute or two talking about non-medical topics with your patient before you launch into the reason for their visit. They will share so much more information with you if they think you are interested in them as a person. Ask about their family, occupation and neighborhood or refer to any special notes the staff lists on the in-take form. This opens up communication and lets the patient *feel* more comfortable with you. It builds trust with them and you may even learn something important. Perhaps he/she is a member of the media or their sister owns a hair salon.

## Mirroring

Mirror the patient's breathing, posture, tonality and gestures:

- If the patient is talking fast – you talk fast.

- If the patient is speaking loudly – you speak loudly.

- If the patient is quiet, shy and meek – slow things down.

- If they cross their legs, you cross your legs.

- Sit eye to eye with the patient.

If you do this correctly, your patient will *feel* bonded to you. They will *feel* like you understand them and can read their thoughts.

Remember: this is an emotional decision. Most women use their intuition to decide who the perfect physician is for them. And, the perfect physician is the one that makes them *feel*:

- Special

- Heard

- Understood

- Important

## Step 3: Uncover the Problem

Understand the patient's current situation by asking open-ended questions such as:

- *"What can I help you with today?"*

- *"What seems to be bothering you?"*

- *"What brings you in to see me?"*

Actively listen. While they are telling you, nod, look at them and take notes so they know you are listening carefully.

You are trying to understand their reasons and perceptions as to why they think they need your services. Find out what their specific concerns are and what motivates them to resolve those issues. Ask probing questions and listen to their responses. Let them talk. Acknowledge you heard them by repeating back what you heard.

## Step 4: Attach Emotions to the Problem and Solution

Be sure to get them emotionally involved. Ask them additional qualifying questions that speak to their emotions such as:

- *"How long has this bothered you?"*

- *"How does this impact your relationships, work, etc.?"*

- *"Why didn't you seek help sooner?"*

- *"How do you envision this improving your life?"*

You want them to "feel" the benefits of your services. Find out how big the problem is and how it affects their life. You need to attach strong emotional reasons for wanting a change. If they say they want to look younger, ask them how looking younger will improve their life. Be sure they "feel" the pay-off.

Allow them to answer your questions completely. It can be very tempting to interrupt with your solution but you'll get more of their attention if you first give them your undivided attention. And always show respect for the patient. Even though you are the expert and know more, arrogance does not sell. If you come across as demeaning, condescending or intimidating you'll drive the prospective patient away. Use words they understand, be concise, and keep it simple. Repeat back briefly to the patient the main points you heard. Ask if you have left anything out – then wait for their answer!

## Step 5: Know Where You Stand

You want to probe with the following questions to qualify the patient to determine where they are in their process:

- *"What is your timeframe?"*

- *"Do you have any other time constraints?"*

- *"Have you done any research on this procedure?"*

- *"What do you already know about this treatment?"*

Ask other open-ended questions to determine how they will reach a decision such as:

- *"What is most important to you when picking a surgeon?"*

- *"What are you looking for in an aesthetic physician?"*

- *"Have you seen any other doctors and, if so, what can I tell you that you don't already know?"*

The answers will help you determine how much time and effort to put into your consultation as well as what approach to take.

## Step 6: Learning Styles for Educating Your Patient

The patients surveyed knew their expectations were met, their concerns were addressed and recommendations explained when you presented your message in a way that best got through to them in the way they understood it most effectively.

There are three different learning styles: Visual, Auditory and Kinesthetic:

- Visual people want to see the results;

- Auditory people want to hear about the results; and

- Kinesthetic people want to touch and feel the results.

All of us have elements of all three modes but usually one mode dominates.

To keep it simple just be sure you incorporate all three modes of learning styles when communicating to your patients using tools such as:

- Photos of other patient results they can "see"

- Videos or telephone conversations with happy patients they can "hear"

- Breast implants and photo albums they can "touch"

## Step 7: Manage Expectations

> *Golden Rule: Under Promise and Over Deliver*

It is your job to ensure the patient has an experience equal to what was promised to them. When your patient's aspirations are headed for perfection, you both lose. Make sure their expectations and reasons for having cosmetic enhancement are based in reality. Have them look at all aspects of their life – both good and bad. Cosmetic enhancement won't bring their spouse back or get them a job promotion. It has boundaries and limitations and is only one facet to their personal fulfillment and self esteem.

Using the following methods, show and tell what you can do for the aesthetic patient. These tools will help you communicate realistic expectations the patient can see, feel and touch:

- Mirror, hand and Q-Tip

- Draw a picture if you're artistic

- Show updated before/after photos of similar patients

- Perform computer imaging and/or skin analysis

- Have them speak to patients and staff members who have had similar procedures

- Show them videos of the procedure (not too graphic)

- Let them touch breast implants, skin care products, etc.

- Tell them about articles you've written and talks you've given

- Use metaphors, analogies and anecdotal experiences of other patients to relay information

Resources: www.ProfectMedical.com
www.Understand.com

## Best Case/Worse Case Scenario

A great way to set expectations is to use the best case-worst case scenario. For example, if the patient is asking you how long the recovery will take, you can respond by saying,

*"The best case scenario is that you will be back to work within one week; however, some patients need an extra week or two".*

Or, let them know that 4 out of 5 patients go back to work within one week. That way, if they are not the "best case" or the "4 out of 5," at least they will recall that you did mention this could happen.

> *If you tell them ahead of time it's an explanation.*
>
> *If you tell them afterwards it's an excuse.*

## Step 8: Differentiate Yourself

It's important to qualify and differentiate yourself by establishing your value; especially if the patient is consulting with several physicians before deciding. Some helpful suggestions include:

- Look the patient in the eye to let them know you are confident in your skill to give them a good result;

- Inform them you have done many of these procedures with excellent results and have very satisfied patients;

- Tell them about any papers you've written or talks you've given on this very procedure; and

- Let them know how many years experience you have doing this procedure or about any special equipment you have to ensure a good result.

Let them know you understand their concerns and fears so they trust you and your recommendations. Reassure them you can meet their expectations and they are in good hands.

Note: If they mention they have spoken with your competition – do not denigrate your colleagues! Stay professional and reiterate your strengths. Mention whatever differentiates you in a positive light without tearing down your competitors. The prospective patient will appreciate and respect your professionalism.

> For Detailed Modules on Differentiating You Practice Visit:
> www.CosmeticImageMarketing.com/noriskoffer

## Step 9: Reassure the Patient

Your patients need reassurance you are the right physician for them and they will get a good result. They want you to be confident about your skills and they also want a little prodding from you so they feel you are competent and will deliver. Simple phrases can help:

*"Sara, you are the perfect candidate for this procedure."*

*"Connie, we have something to work with here and I'm sure you will be pleased with the outcome."*

> Several patients surveyed commented while they were not looking for a sales pitch, they were looking for confidence the physician would do a good job. If the physician was being too conservative, some of the patients took that as timidity and were not convinced of their competence.

## Step 10: Closing

Consider a prepared closing statement. You can say it before you hand the prospective patient back to the patient care coordinator to discuss particulars and schedule the procedure.

By the way, the patients may want to negotiate pricing with you and play on your heartstrings. To avoid this, it's best not to discuss finances with the patient and to play dumb. The best way to handle money is to call your nurse or patient care coordinator back in to discuss this while you are saying,

> *"Nancy handles that part so I'll let her give you all the details".*

You should not need to rely on heavy closing statements if everything else up to this point was done correctly and professionally. The patient you bonded with who was treated well, had his/her fears calmed and questions answered should be ready to take the next step. If you created a safe, comfortable, competent experience, the patient should be ready. Keep it conversational by escorting them back to your patient care coordinator while saying,

> *"It was great to meet you Sally. Sara can fill you in on the details to your questions and I look forward to seeing you again soon."*

## Step 11: Give Them a Good Result

It's important to carry through with a good result and a pleasant-enough experience. Remember, if the above steps were followed, the patient is looking for a "good" result, not a "fantastic-result-that-changes-her-universe" result.

## Step 12: Follow-Up

Call the patient to see how they are doing. Answer any questions they may have and reassure them all went well and they will be fine. If they had an invasive procedure, reiterate what they can expect for the next few days and that your staff will be calling to check in on them and report back to you. Mention you look forward to seeing them again in your office for their post-op appointments or their next treatment.

# COMPLICATION/DISSATISFACTION AFTER SURGERY

> *"My surgeon was always "in surgery" when I called to talk about how unhappy I was with the asymmetry I got from my surgery and I ended up going to another doctor to fix it."*
>
> — *Sam, 43 years old - Breast Aug*

Every office experiences patients who are not absolutely thrilled with their result. It's a reality and you just need to deal with it professionally.

It came up several times in the survey that a patient felt uncomfortable discussing their dissatisfaction with their physician since they were not being well received. Some of the physicians dismissed their patients' concerns by saying it will just take time and they need to be patient. But remember: you are not the one walking around looking and feeling disfigured. An unhappy patient does not want to hear "be patient." They want you to do something! Reassure them, comfort them, offer them an interim solution – do something they can hang on to and "do" while they are healing. Some physicians were so averse to dealing with negativity. Often, the patient had trouble seeing them again when the patient wanted to schedule some follow-up time to discuss their concerns.

Please don't ignore a problem. It seldom goes away and can grow into a much bigger problem and become litigious if not handled properly. Minimally, it can create bad word-of-mouth comments about you and hurt your reputation in the community.

# THE DECISION-MAKING PROCESS

A recurring theme in the survey results indicated patients were more confused after they visited physicians, researched the topic and read media reports. Many found it daunting to sort out the conflicting information collected supposedly to help them make the best and safest decision.

Know how difficult this process can be for your patients. Your prospective patient wants to change something. They feel bad or uncomfortable and they hope fixing, repairing, or enhancing it will make them feel better. They feel vulnerable and are looking to you for help.

That said it's important to note that patients want to avoid making a bad choice. Their goal is to look at the risks and the ways to minimize them. They do not want to regret their decision. A major part of your job is to reassure them they are in the right place for the right procedure and they will be happy with the result.

> If a prospective patient is afraid or confused, they will decide to do nothing. It's your job to help them make the right decision.

# WHAT IS THE AESTHETIC PATIENT REALLY BUYING?

What are your patients really buying? You probably think they are buying your expertise. But they can't really tell how skilled you are since they know nothing about medicine. All they have to go on are clues: your reputation, your past results, your marketing materials, your staff, etc. In other words, your expertise is assumed and they are really buying you.

And psychologically, they are buying hope. They are buying happiness. They are buying the hope of happiness. The aesthetic patient believes looking better will improve their lives and they will feel better. They want to know you are the right physician for them and can make that happen.

## TYPES OF CONSUMERS

Consumer behavior is a complex subject and involves emotions, personalities and life experiences. To understand your patients and their motives better, here are four groups of typical aesthetic patients that will make up your practice:

### Tire Kickers

This group doesn't know what they want. They seem to have a lot of time on their hands because they attend your events, eat your food, take your samples and never, ever buy. They may even book a consultation, go through the motions, but never book a procedure. Do not exert energy on this group since they can waste much of your time if you let them.

## Deal Makers/Price Shoppers

This group is looking for the best deal in town above all else. They have a tendency to regard cosmetic enhancement as a commodity and will spend much of their consultation negotiating with you and your staff. To them it's an art form to get you to lower your prices or throw in freebies. Beware of them. They will tell their friends they got a great deal from you just because they asked for one. This will set a bad precedent in your practice. And if they came for price, they will leave for price so this is not where you want to spend your time and resources.

## Brand Loyalists

This is your preferred group. They love you and would not go to anyone else. They wouldn't even consider going to anyone else – even if their fees were half of yours! They are your cheerleaders and your advocates. Treat them well and they are yours for life. Most of your efforts should be concentrated on this group and growing it to include their loyal friends, family and colleagues. These people consider you to be a friend and will sing your praises to anyone interested. Be sure they feel appreciated and acknowledged for their efforts in spreading your word. They are invaluable to you when growing an aesthetic practice.

## Luxury Innovators/Quality Shoppers

While this group wants only the best and will pay for it, they can be a pain in the butt. They want everything their way. You need to drop everything to stroke their egos. They have a tendency to flaunt their status and expect better treatment than your other patients. While you should treat all of your patients with respect and special care, spending a little extra time and effort on this group can pay off. Like-minded people know other like-minded people. This can be a profitable group to appease – but not at the expense of your brand loyalists.

# HOW DECISIONS ARE REACHED

The decision-making process is an entire subject on its own; however, here are some basics to remember:

- Decisions are quickly reached, then justified.

- People act on prejudices, habits and past experience much more than on knowledge.

- It takes a patient a split second to make a decision but getting ready to make that decision can take a long time.

People make decisions because it looks right, feels right, sounds right or makes sense to them:

## Looks-Right People

These people make decisions based on what they see and then they visualize how it will look for them. Show them lots of before/after photos and/or computer imaging and skin analysis results. Give them visuals since they trust what they see.

## Sounds-Right People

These people make decisions based on what they hear. When they hear words making sense to them, they respond well. Tell them about the procedure with confidence and sincerity. Have your staff and other patients tell them about their own experiences. Paint them a mental picture with words.

## Feels-Right People

These people make decisions based on what they can physically feel and they will literally feel a sensation in their body that tells them it feels right. Give them product samples and let them try on breast implants. Let them touch and feel your patient information packet and your brochures.

## Makes-Sense People

These people need reasons for what they do. Answer the "why" for them. Give them facts, data and reasons so they can justify their decision in their own minds.

# AVERAGE SALES CYCLE

The average sales cycle from the time the patients that were surveyed contemplated cosmetic surgery to the time they booked was 2-4 years. And when they were finally ready, they wanted it NOW!

The average sales cycle for minimally invasive procedures was 1-2 years. And again, when they were finally ready, they wanted it NOW!

While it may have seemed like they were being impulsive, most of the aesthetic patients had been contemplating procedures for a while and they were ready to act on it.

# PRICING

The majority of those surveyed said repeatedly they were not looking for the cheapest price but rather a fair price and a good result. They were, however, insulted when the price was outrageously higher than the others.

Also, most had "sticker shock" during their first consultation. It's important your patients understand you are competitive with the others in your area so they won't feel compelled to shop around.

And, be sure to offer financing options to take the sting out of a big-ticket item. Reiterate they can have it now rather than wait until they have saved up enough which could be years or never. Wouldn't they prefer to have that quality of life now rather than wait?

Be sure they understand that you price your services by the years you have been in practice – especially if you have been around longer and have more patients to show for it. Sell experience since it's valuable. Most patients don't want to be guinea pigs.

Sell "value-added" rather than "cheaper." If you are more expensive than your competitors, explain why. Your price includes post surgery garments, pain and anti-bruising medications, your personal cell phone number in case of emergencies and anything else you can think of to ensure the patient has a pleasant experience. Once the patient understands you are truly offering a complete "pleasant patient experience," they are not as likely to compare you to the others. When in doubt, charge a bit more than the others. There's a huge percentage of the population where price creates perception of quality, so go for it.

Also, most patients want a discount on multiple procedures so you may want to allow for that. Be sure you can explain how combination therapies or the OR time, anesthesia, etc., will be cheaper if more is done at the same time. Be able to show them the savings. It's also helpful to prepare your quotes on the computer and produce a printout rather than to handwrite them. The patient is less likely to negotiate with computer printouts.

## NEGOTIATING

The well-informed patient has done some price shopping, may have other quotes and is prepared to negotiate with you. Prepare your comeback while you are calm and thinking clearly. Don't quip back off the top of your head to the aesthetic patient who is asking for a discount. You may say something you'll regret, talk badly about your colleagues or say something inappropriate or alienating to the patient.

If the patient tells you they've seen someone else and they are $1,000 cheaper, your response or your patient care coordinator's response could be:

*"The doctor's prices are based on his years of expertise. He has per-formed this particular procedure many times and has even trained other physicians on it so I'm confident you will get the best result from him at this reasonable price."*

## OTHER NEGOTIATING STRATEGIES

<u>Use competition in the reverse.</u> Let the prospective patient know you have several other prospective patients wanting to use your services. If they don't book, others will and they may have to wait months before you have another opening. You must be willing to risk the sale. You win some - you lose some - but you'll win more if they perceive scarcity.

<u>Use the power of investment.</u> If the patient invests their time, money (consultation fee) and energy into you, they are more likely to see it through, especially when discussing something as emotional as cosmetic enhancement. Cope with price at the end of the negotiation after the patient has committed time and energy in your office. If they bring it up early, acknowledge it, chat about it and then put off the specifics until later if at all possible. The patient's time investment will cause them to become more flexible at the end of the process that included the initial consultation with staff, viewing photo books, talking with patients or viewing tapes, computer imaging, skin analysis, consultation with doctor and then back to staff for figures.

If you have determined your prices are what they are no matter what, be sure to set the scenario early on so the patient doesn't feel like they have an option to negotiate. Don't negotiate if you have built up your reputation and have many happy patients who are willing to talk with prospective patients. Most patients are not looking for the cheapest price anyway. They are looking for a good experience and the best result at a fair price. You want to set it up so they perceive you as the best and you are worth the price you have determined to be fair.

Having said that, in today's competitive world you may feel compelled to negotiate. Do it with something other than cash – such as superior service! Offer them a complimentary treatment if they buy a package of treatments. Offer to fill and prepare all medications and supplies ahead of time for the patient so they don't have to bother with it. The intent here is to include more value-added amenities so the patient feels like they are getting preferential treatment or more for less.

## USE ADDED VALUE

Rather than discount your prices, simply add more value for the same price. For example, when your patient purchases a packages of (5) Parisian Peel treatments, they get 15 units of Botox or every injectable procedure gets a Free Parisian Peel treatment or every injectable procedure includes a Free gel pack for the patient to take home.

If it's a surgical procedure, offer to include post-op treatments to help with healing and scarring at no charge (Cimeosil and GelZone Wrap for healing and scarring).

The point is to offer more value so the patient is happy without hurting your profit margins and that makes you happy.

Resources: www.ParisianPeel.com
www.Implantech.com
www.GioPelle.com

# CASH VS. CARECREDIT

Rather than explain to the patient you charge extra for them to use CareCredit financing, turn it around. Tell them about your cash discount instead. This way, it's a positive rather than a negative and your profit margins will be higher.

> *Resources: www.CareCredit.com*

# COMPUTER IMAGING

There is nothing more compelling than an aesthetic patient seeing themselves and their very own sun damage, signs of aging and possibilities of what things could be. The more you can personalize the patient's concerns and possible results - the better.

Using today's technology such as computer imaging helps you articulate and visualize the patient's concern as well as what the solution could look like.

The technology becomes a helpful sales tool if used correctly. It's not about misleading – it's about educating the patient. It's about communicating what you hear the patient says is their concern and then showing them what that could look like. Your interpretation of "a little" and the patient's can be quite different and computer imaging can clarify what each of you means.

> *96% of those surveyed would have liked computer imaging or skin analysis*

# COMPLEXION ANALYSIS SYSTEM

A complexion analysis system provides quantitative measurement and analysis of visible and non-visible skin concerns with multi-dimensional views. This type of system provides objective information about the condition of the patient's own skin. It reveals the damage to the skin because of age, genetics and sun exposure. Also, the system can show what the skin would look like after treatment. Again, when used properly, this is a very helpful communications and sales tool.

> *Resource: www.ProfectMedical.com*

# BEFORE/AFTER PHOTOGRAPHS

The patients want and need to see their before and after photos. It's amazing what aesthetic medicine can do for them and you want to give them a visual so they show and tell their friends, family and colleagues. Today's technology can show face as well as body images to help you promote a complete array of skin, face and body solutions.

> *Resource: www.ProfectMedical.com*

# PRE-OP SURGICAL CONSULTATION APPOINTMENT

If the patient books surgery, the pre-operative and surgical appointments need to be booked and a deposit needs to be collected. The pre-operative appointment is important and comprehensive. The patient must completely understand the risks; the informed consent documents and very thorough pre- and post-operative instructions and information so there are no surprises. Although it seems like they are listening, have them read the rules out loud so they know not to take aspirin for a specified amount of time, that they must have a friend take them home, and should have medications ahead of time, etc. There should not be any unpleasant surprises later while they tell you they didn't know something. The anesthesiologist also needs to call ahead to prepare the patient and discuss anesthesia and surgical preparation.

## AMENITIES

Offering extra services to help your patient be as comfortable as possible helps you stand out as a truly caring professional. Services such as cab/limo service to and from the office, 24/7 nursing care, hotel accommodations and meals delivered during recovery all lead to a wonderful recuperation your patients will remember and brag about for years to come. Again, success is in the details.

## "ADD-ON" PROCEDURES

Your patients may call back to "add on" to their surgery. They have gone home and decided since they are already going through the process; they might as well add another area to be liposuctioned for example. Be sure to explain you will mail or fax them a revised quote with new numbers so they realize you don't do this for free. For example, several of the patients interviewed didn't think they would be charged if they added a little liposuction to their "love handles" as long as they were getting liposuction on their stomach. They were surprised to learn it would add thousands of dollars. Just be sure your patient care coordinator knows to say:

*"Sure Sally, we can add that and just know that increases the OR time, the anesthesiologist's time as well as the doctor's time so that will be an additional $2,000. You're smart to do this now because it's cheaper than waiting and doing it separately later."*

Most patients don't mind paying more as long as they understand the extra charge and that it is customary no matter who does the procedure. You do not want them shopping around again. Always explain why things cost as much as they do since most laymen cannot believe it could cost much more for a little "add-on." As long as they know it's much cheaper for them to add on now rather than wait and do a separate procedure at a separate time, they will most likely agree to it.

# POST-OP CARE AFTER SURGERY

*"I was super swollen and a little freaked out but my doctor and his staff checked in with me regularly to reassure me that all would be well and I really appreciated that."*

*— Nancy, 44 years old - Bleph and Laser Resurfacing*

Those surveyed said a lot about their care after their surgery - both good and bad. This is a sensitive time for the patient and can be an emotional roller coaster. Recuperating from a cosmetic surgical procedure can be uncomfortable, painful, disheartening and depressing. The patient might have regret at this point since they may look swollen and bruised. Even though you have told them about the downtime, they might not have understood it as well as they do now that they are going through it first-hand.

> *Resources: www.Implantech.com (Cimeosil for scars and Gelzone wraps)*
> *www.GioPelle.com (Gel Packs and Camouflage Kits)*

Follow-up is a crucial step and can lead to or away from word-of-mouth referrals. The post-operative care must be as stringent as the pre-operative care since this is what distinguishes you from the others. This is what tells the patient you care about them as a patient as well as a person and shows your character, integrity and compassion. Following up with your post-surgical patient is crucial – not only to be sure

they are comfortable but also to ensure they have a positive experience throughout the entire process. Patient satisfaction is your optimum goal. Happy patients refer their friends, family and colleagues and happy patients don't sue or bad-talk you. Here are some suggestions:

- Physician should personally call the patient the first evening to see how they are and reiterate what to expect over the next few days.

- The staff can call the following days to check in on the patient to answer any questions and reassure the patient they will be fine.

- The physician should see the patient back in the office 1-4 times for follow-up appointments, depending on the procedure and the patient.

- Staff should be diligent about getting testimonials and taking photographs and getting consents to show these photographs to other prospective patients.

Some physicians actually give surgical patients their cell phone number and urge them to call if any concerns arise or they have a need to talk.

Some physicians make house calls to check on patients and possibly remove their stitches. While this might seem excessive, this really stands out and the patients will tell their family, friends and colleagues about your great service.

## POST-OP GIFT

When those surveyed were asked if they would have appreciated flowers while recuperating, the responses were mixed. While most of the patients thought it would have been special to receive flowers at their home while they were recuperating, others thought it was too personal and was an added cost to their bill since it was probably worked into the fees. Some thought a fruit basket would have been more appropriate than flowers.

Use your judgment on this and decide what image you are portraying. Some offices use this beautifully to continue to bond with the patient and the patients love it. Other offices may not get a good response from this if their in-office processes were not up to par.

If you cater to a certain group that you are sure would enjoy a token of your appreciation and concern for their comfort, then by all means send flowers or fruit. Frankly, it will separate you from your competitors since most don't go this extra mile. It could win you increased word-of-mouth referrals as well.

## POST-OP PHOTOGRAPHS

> *"I was so happy with my result; I showed my photos to several of my friends and family."*
>
> — *Christine, 44 years old – Botox, Fillers and Laser*

A creative and subtle way to increase your word-of-mouth referrals is to hand to your post-operative patient a thank you note with their before and after photographs. This gives them the choice to show the photos to their family, friends and colleagues. The timing is important since they will be most excited about spreading the word while it's all still new so don't delay. If they are happy with their result, they will most likely be excited to "show and tell" and sing your praises to others. Be sure your name and telephone number is on the thank you note to prompt them to call you.

## POST-OP PATIENT EXPERIENCE

> *"I never saw the doctor again and it made me feel as if I were just another surgery."*
>
> — *Cynthia, 48 years old – Bleph*

Several of those surveyed said they felt truly dismissed by the physician when the procedure was completed. This is a huge mistake. If you take care of your patient afterwards, they will feel so bonded to you, your staff and your practice, they will shout your name from the rooftops because they have had such a great experience and got such a wonderful result.

You are never "done" with your aesthetic patient. To bond even further with your patient and to ensure they get the ultimate result, offer a follow-up treatment from your staff. If they had a face lift, offer them a makeup session to help them cover up redness while they recuperate. If they've had liposuction, offer an endermologie treatment to help in the healing process, etc. This shows them you still care about them as

135

a patient even after their procedure. It can also lead to further procedures, product sales and word-of-mouth referrals.

Several patients surveyed commented they liked when you, the physician, requested follow-up visits. They were impressed you cared enough to want to see them again in person to check on their progress. While this is an opportunity to take before/after photos, it's also a time to solidify your relationship with the patient and ask for referrals and testimonials in a casual, professional way.

Be assured if you treat the patients well, or even better afterwards, they will be your advocates for life. They will return for more cosmetic enhancement and introduce you to their friends, family and colleagues.

## POST-OP SURGICAL PATIENT SURVEY

The best way to learn what your surgical patients think and want is to ask them. The best time to ask them is when they have had a recent experience with you and your office. Mailing a simple follow-up survey to your surgical patient is an excellent way to learn what you are doing well and what could be done better. Wait until they are completely healed and fully recuperated. Keep it simple and ask open-ended questions such as:

- Why did you choose me?

- How were you treated before/during/after your surgery?

- What could we do better?

- How do you feel about your result?

- Would you recommend our office to others?

Be sure to leave space for their free-flowing comments. Make these surveys anonymous and add them to your testimonial binder so your prospective patients can read about you first-hand. This works extremely well and can lead to a much higher closing ratio since the patient feels more comfortable after reading an album full of patient accolades.

Your patient's satisfaction is the distance between the care they expected and the care they received. So this is great feedback to help you improve your processes. It can even alert you to concerns you may need to address such as an unfriendly staff member or a chaotic atmosphere that needs to be streamlined.

> Download a free post-op surgery survey at:
> http://www.CosmeticImageMarketing.com/postopsurvey

## PATIENT POST-OP TESTIMONIAL VIDEO

If a picture is worth a thousand of words, then a video is worth ten thousand! As long as the patient is standing in front of you and telling you how happy they are with their result, capture them on video. Keep a simple-to-use Flip Video Camcorder in your drawer. Ask your patient if they wouldn't mind repeating what they just told you about their initial problem, why they chose you and what you did for them. Be sure they give you their permission (in writing) to use their video in your promotional efforts such as on your Website, your internal monitors and in your email marketing.

> Resource: www.flipcamera.com

# ASK FOR REFERRALS

The best time to ask for referrals is when the patient is happy with you. This can be immediately following a procedure such as an injectable or at the patient's surgical post-op appointment when they are completely healed and loving their result. Take advantage of this time to ask for referrals. It can be as simple as saying:

> *"Karen, we would love to help other patients just like you, so please tell your friends about us and we'll be sure to take good care of them."*

This is also the perfect time to take post-op photos and hand them a set so they can not only see the result, they can also share them with family, friends and colleagues. Be sure your name and telephone number are on the photos to prompt them to contact you.

# FOLLOW-UP IN GENERAL

Follow-up is the one main action item that is often neglected, ignored or resisted; yet one of the most important steps in your process. You may be short staffed or you just don't make it a priority; however, <u>this is the one area where you can make more money in less time than almost anything else you do.</u>

Think about it: the prospective patient was interested enough to call you, ask questions, answer your questions, book a consultation and take time away from their busy life to meet with you. They have already invested in you. Why wouldn't you follow-up to see how they are and if they are ready to take the next step? It takes less than a minute to make the telephone call. Think of it this way – that follow-up telephone call could be worth $40,000 - $98,000 to you (see the value of a patient section)!

138

Your staff may tell you that it's not professional to follow up – you are not selling cars – you are selling hope, etc. Frankly, people are people no matter what they are buying. They want to know you care about them and want to do business with them.

Follow up with a letter or thank you note, wait 3-4 days and then make a telephone call. If you have to leave a message, tell them to call you back if they are interested or you will add them to the tickler file to call one more time within two weeks. If they answer the telephone, ask them if they are ready to move forward. If they say no, ask them if you should follow up again and when. They will tell you and you will get a sense of where they are in the process, especially if they say, "I'm not sure and I'll call you when I'm ready." At that point, you don't want to call again. Simply add them to your database as a prospective patient and they can receive periodic mailings such as your practice newsletter or special promotions and invite them to your events.

If you are going to invest your time, administrative costs and marketing dollars towards PR, marketing and advertising, make the most of it by following up at every step in the process.

Follow up:

- with a patient information packet after speaking to a caller

- with a patient call to ensure they received the information packet with a patient telephone call reminding them of their scheduled appointment

- with a telephone call after a missed appointment so the patient can reschedule

- with a thank you letter/call after new patient visit

- with a thank you letter/call after purchase of treatment or procedure

- with a thank you letter/call after patient refers another patient

- after the surgical patient is examined and is considering surgery*

- the evening following the procedure/surgery

- after surgery the following day

- after surgery the day after that, etc.

- with post-op satisfaction questionnaire

- with those patients who haven't been back for awhile**

*The rule of thumb for following up with a patient who is considering surgery is to use the "three strikes and you're out" rule. Follow up once with a letter right away, then a post-consultation telephone call and then one additional follow-up call. If they don't respond, they can now be put in your database to receive future mailings, offers and invitations to your practice.

**There are excellent software programs available on the market today to help you automate and simplify the follow-up process.

Resources: www.PatientNOW.com

# KEEP IN TOUCH

Be sure to keep in touch with your patients. An aesthetic patient will usually have several cosmetic procedures performed in their lifetime. Be sure all or most are performed by you. Send them informative newsletters, invitations to your events as well as special promotions. The true aesthetic patient is always looking for ways to look and feel better. Keep them "in the loop" and they will continue to visit you regularly for upkeep – and they'll bring their friends.

Resource: www.SmileReminder.com

# PRIVACY

The HIPAA rules are strict and must be followed. Be sure all privacy and confidentiality rules are maintained when leaving messages and sending personal medical information through the mail. Use a discreet envelope and/or telephone message.

But know that you are well within your rights to promote your services to your patients and prospective patients unless they indicate otherwise.

# IX

# MARKETING PLAN AND BUDGET

An important part of your business plan is marketing your practice. A plan for attracting patients and then keeping them is vital to your success. Look at marketing as a revenue-generating line item because it will be if done correctly.

How much should you spend on marketing? Investing 10-15% of your gross revenues is the norm for those who want to grow their practice and less for those mature practices that just want to maintain their current practice database.

You may think marketing is simply advertising, but I assure you, it's much more. Marketing encompasses every detail of your practice - the office furnishings, the visit with you, the entire patient experience, and the on-going communications with your patients. Marketing is every "touch" you have with your patient – good or bad – that helps them decide if you are the right physician for them now and in the future. Your target is the ever-changing emotional aesthetic patient who will continually examine if the services you provide are worth the time, money and effort to them. Marketing you and your practice helps ensure they continue to answer "yes."

# IN-HOUSE MARKETING

> *"I was in my dermatologist's office for Botox and noticed a framed article she had written about liposuction. I asked her about it, we talked and I had it done the next month. I love my flat tummy!*
>
> — Amy, 42 years old - Botox and Liposuction

Education through "ask me about tools" is a subtle way to market your aesthetic practice. Displaying a mention of procedures throughout your office for your visiting patients to see and ask about is necessary. These marketing tools should educate your current patients on every product, procedure and treatment you provide. Tell your patients what you offer so they don't wander off to someone else's office because they didn't know you provided that service! Do it in a subtle, professional way so they will feel comfortable and at ease asking to learn more about what you can offer them.

## "SUBTLE SELLING" TOOLS

It is said physicians and staff are not sales people and are uncomfortable with the sales process. While you should never push a patient to do or buy, you should let the patient know you are confident and competent to help them with their aesthetic concerns. There are simple, subtle tools you can use to professionally promote your services without pressure.

Here are easy-to-implement in-house marketing tools to help:

## Patient Photo Albums

> *"The physician had huge books full of before/after photos. I knew that he had lots of experience and was probably very good since so many others had gone to him.*
>
> *— Stephanie, 29 years old – Breast Aug*

Use a good digital camera to take digital photos that are easier to archive and more accessible for future use. Use a variety of patient demographics (age, gender and ethnicity) so prospective patients can relate to them. And, be sure the photos are current.

Use your own before/after patient photos versus using your vendors'. Your own unique photos should be bound in high quality, sturdy, leather books. Matte-finish inserts cut down on the glare and are easier to view than plastic covers over photos. Be sure to add a disclaimer at the beginning of the album stating everyone in the book agreed to his or her photos being shown. Be sure that's true and you have their approval!

*Resource: www.ProfectMedical.com*

## Procedural Digital Photo Frames

Procedural picture frames are now available for passive patient education in your exam rooms. You can run your power point presentations on them and update them easily. They are a silent picture show of your before/after photos with descriptions of procedures your patients can ask you about when you enter the room.

Resources: www.Costco.com
www.DigiFrames.com
www.bestbuy.com

## Testimonials in Leather-Bound Book

It's not what YOU say about you,

it's what YOUR PATIENTS say about you that really counts.

It's very compelling for your prospective patients to read comments and accolades about you from your current patients who took the time to provide feedback. I assure you, your job becomes much easier when a prospective patient repeatedly reads how wonderful you are and how happy your patients are with you and their results. To collect testimonials simply send each post-op patient a survey after they are fully rejuvenated. Include "yes" and "no" questions but also provide space for free-hand comments. Then display them in beautiful, leather-bound albums. The more surveys - the better.

Download a free patient satisfaction survey at
http://www.CosmeticImageMarketing.com/postopsurvey

## "Meet the Doctor"

Have a "Meet the Doctor" glossy sheet prominently displayed so they can see your credentials, photo, associations, accomplishments, etc., all on one page. Your patients will not only be impressed, they will be clearer about what differentiates you from the others. It's a great way to indirectly blow your own horn.

*See sample at http://www.CosmeticImageMarketing.com/meetthedoctor*

## Display PR Efforts

*"He had been on TV and in our local newspaper so I knew he was good."*

*— Sandy, 28 years old – Laser*

Any time you are quoted, filmed, taped or written about, be sure your patients and prospective patients know about it. You can create 4-color, glossy PR pieces called "Doctor in the News" to be prominently displayed in your reception area and exam rooms and handed out in your patient information packets. Be sure to add them to your website, newsletters and direct mail as well.

*See sample at http://www.CosmeticImageMarketing.com/prslicks*

## Procedure Videos

Running a video about your services on a video player or flat screen wall monitor in your reception area is a great educational tool. If done professionally, it's a wonderful introduction and indicates to the aesthetic patient you are serious about quality and education. It sets the tone for a positive visit. It will help educate patients on procedures they might not know you offer and it's a good "ask me about" tool to cross promote all of your services.

Keep in mind; however, it may agitate some patients if they feel they are being oversold so audibly and visually. Your laundry list of procedures may hold limited interest to them. They may prefer to see an outline of procedures and then choose for themselves what they prefer to learn more about. Also, if kept waiting too long, the loop may be repeating itself and becoming annoying.

I suggest offering patients headsets and/or setting up a monitor with a list of procedures to allow the patient to learn more about the procedure(s) they are interested in. You can also loop a silent power point presentation giving just the name of the procedure and the before and after photos. The patient then has the choice to watch or not watch the screen.

> Resources: www.Understand.com
> www.WaitMediaGroup.com

## Video of You and Your Practice

The more the prospective patient feels they know you, the more likely they are to pick you over your competitors. Showing a video about you, your philosophy, expertise, office and staff gives them a good idea of who you are and what you value. It can also pave the way for a more relaxed, friendly consultation since they feel as if you have already met.

The professionally-produced video should be on your website to help gain more prospective patients through the Internet who are surfing for an aesthetic physician. It can also be shown in your office before a new patient consultation. If you are in a high foot traffic area, you can also show it outside your building to drive new patients in to learn more. And, you can mass-produce the video on mini CD's to be mailed and passed out to prospective patients.

> Resource: www.PracticeProfitsMedia.com

## Video Patient Testimonials

The best referral comes from a satisfied patient. Capture their comments for other patients to see and hear. Use a professional to do the videotaping or if you have a good quality video camera and someone who understands lighting, you can make your own videos of post-op patients singing your praises. You can then loop them on a computer monitor for the prospective patient to view. Add them to your website as well.

# IN-HOUSE SIGNAGE

Every single person who walks through your door should know about every treatment, procedure and product you offer. Have you ever heard a patient say, "I didn't know you did that!" and they had it done by your competitor? To avoid that type of response, be sure you have the following tools readily available:

## Vendor Marketing Kits

When you purchase products and services from your vendors, they typically include their marketing kit to help you promote their services and products to your patients. The kit may include posters, patient brochures, lapel pins, FAQ's, samples of press releases, ads and before/after photos. Start there.

## Retail Displays and Samples

Retail displays are also a great way to cross promote products to your aesthetic patient. They will be most tempted to buy if you let them see, touch and feel samples and testers so have them readily available.

> Resource: www.FlipCamera.com

## Customized Practice Brochure

Design your own customized practice brochure outlining your credentials, services, philosophy and policies. Include photos of you, your staff and your office. Also include your "look and feel" such as your logo, graphics and colors so the reader gets a good sense of who you are and what you value.

> Resource: www.CosmeticImageMarketing.com

## Customized Practice Poster

Using your same "look and feel" from your brochure and website, design large posters to display in each exam room outlining every procedure, treatment and product you provide. Make them eye-catching so the patient comments on them. This opens up a discussion about other aesthetic procedures you offer.

> Resource: www.CosmeticImageMarketing.com

# COSMETIC QUESTIONNAIRE

The first time a patient visits your office include a simple cosmetic survey along with your in-take form. Ask the question,

*"What concerns you?"*

Then list each concern and let them check them off, i.e., age spots, wrinkles, sun damage, rosacea, cellulite, sagging jowls, etc.

You, the physician, can then comment on the survey during the consultation. Ask the patient if they would like to learn more about simple and painless solutions to their particular skin problems.

> *Download a free sample at*
> *http://www.CosmeticImageMarketing.com/cosmeticsurvey*

# EDUCATIONAL MATERIALS IN THE RECEPTION AREA

Patient education materials such as procedure brochures should be on display in your reception area. You can also have a PC terminal in your reception area showing your website and explaining the various procedures offered. These tools are there to educate your patients about what you can offer them and could save you time during the consultation. Many of their questions may already be answered. These materials will also subtly introduce comparable procedures and treatments the aesthetic patient has not yet considered but could be interested in learning more about.

> *Resources: www.Understand.com*
> *www.WaitMediaGroup.com*

# INTERNAL MARKETING STRATEGIES

Your #1 asset is your patient database. They are your "low-hanging fruit" since they already know you, they like you and hopefully they trust you. And, they are much more apt to respond to your marketing efforts. So, resources are best spent marketing to your current patients and prospective patients whom you've already met. And, once you have spent the time, money and effort getting them through your door, you want to keep them there!

Also, keep in mind it's always a good idea to reconnect with your patients to reactivate them, especially those whom:

- You haven't seen for awhile;

- Who came in for a consultation but never booked; or

- Who need to come back to finish their treatments.

The following strategies work well:

## Introductory Letter to Your Current Database

Using your own letterhead and envelopes, send a personalized, informative letter to your patients outlining something new, perhaps a staff person or a procedure and include a special offer for them to come in to see you.

## Practice Newsletter

Promotion through education is a professional way to keep in touch with your patients. The aesthetic patient does not want to be sold but they do want to be educated. This is a great way to update your patients on what's new in your practice as well as the world of cosmetic enhancement. Inform them of:

- New procedures, treatments or products

- New office hours or staff members

- Upcoming events

- Patient profile with testimonial

- Your newly-designed Website

- Your "Refer-a-Friend" program, gift certificates, and VIP cards

I highly recommend adding a "call to action" prompting the patient to pick up the telephone to learn more and/or make an appointment. You can have a special offer with a tight expiration date so they respond now rather than wait.

You want to send your quarterly or semi-annual newsletter to your current patients and also to neighboring salons, spas and retailers who share your demographics as well as other non-competing specialties with whom you would like to align.

Be sure the newsletter looks professional and is customized to your practice so it differentiates you from all the others.

Resource: www.CosmeticImageMarketing.com

## Direct Mail Marketing

Direct mail is still one of the cheapest forms of marketing your aesthetic practice. You send a specific message to a specific patient who already knows you so it's extremely targeted. Communicating with your patients throughout the year is essential in keeping your patients loyal to you in this competitive environment. If you don't keep in touch with them – your competitors will.

Send special event invitations, birthday cards and holiday greetings to show you care about your patients all year (not just when things are slow). Also, target specific messages to the right patient and offer them the motivation to act now. This will build patient loyalty as well as your revenues. For example, send all of your wrinkle filler patients a special offer to try a new, longer-lasting wrinkle filler. Work with your vendors since they will be happy to help you promote their products.

In all patient communications be sure you are addressing benefits and answering the question, "What's in it for me?" so the patient will pay attention and respond.

## Email Marketing

Email marketing is the cheapest form of advertising today and it's instantaneous. If you find yourself in a slow period, you can send out an email message with a special offer and the telephones can ring within minutes. You can also use it to stay in touch with your patients on a consistent basis so they remember you when they are ready for your services.

Because of spamming laws, you must get permission from your patients to communicate via email. You can do this by:

- Asking for their email address on your patient in-take form (i.e., *You can receive exclusive web offers if you provide your email address*);

- Your receptionist should ask each new patient who comes through the door if they would like to receive exclusive offers via email;

- Have a special display at check-out asking again in case they didn't feel comfortable enough when checking in; and

- Your website should capture their email addresses as well.

Since a patient can opt out any time they wish, be sure your email messages are attractive, newsworthy and worthwhile so they see the benefit in receiving them throughout the year. Your email messages should be short, informative, eye-catching, fun and easy to open. I suggest .html format so nobody has to click and wait for it to download.

> Resource: www.CosmeticImageMarketing.com

## Thank You Notes

Thank you notes will distinguish you as a true professional and portray you as a caring, committed physician. Most of your competitors don't send them out since it's another time-consuming step and they may see no value to them. I assure you, most patients will "note" you went the extra mile and will remember you fondly. Frankly, it can't hurt and may help a lot.

The secret to the thank you notes is to do them daily so it doesn't grow into a big job later. Every day, have your staff send out thank you notes to:

- Any prospective patient that visited you that day.

- Any patient that spent a certain amount on products and services.

- Any patient who referred another patient to you, etc.

You need to assign thank you note duty to one or two staff people to ensure it gets done. Your staff needs to understand this is not busy work; this is an important tool in your practice to build patient loyalty and referrals.

Resource: www.CosmeticImageMarketing.com

## Word-of-Mouth Referrals

Word-of-Mouth referrals are where the majority of your revenues should come from. Since patients today talk more freely about their aesthetic enhancements, you should count on more referrals from them. Referrals should be encouraged and sought after.

Why are word-of-mouth referrals so important? Because:

- A referred patient is already 80% sold on you since the patient's friend, family member or colleague has sung your praises;

- The closing ratio will be much higher than if they weren't referred;

- It's free advertising;

- They are not as price sensitive; and

- They are more likely to stay loyal to you.

Your happy patients are your cheerleaders, your advocates and the best sales people imaginable. When they are happy and satisfied with you, they want to brag about you to others. Help them do so with the following ideas:

- Tell them you would like more patients just like them. They should send in their friends, family and colleagues and you will take good care of them.

- Add the phrase "bring a friend" to all of your invitations.

- Add the Website feature, "Send This Page to a Friend."

- Incorporate a "Refer a Friend" program. For example, if they refer a friend, they both get 50% off a certain treatment or a free product (check with your specialty's society by-laws).

- Thank them with a personal telephone call or thank you note for referring to you.

- Send them gift cards they can use towards their next visit.

But remember: patients have to be truly happy and satisfied with the service they receive *every time* – period. The saying goes: "A happy patient tells three people and an unhappy patient tells 10."

> Be sure every single patient has a 'WOW' experience every time they are in contact with you, your staff and your office.

## Frequent Referrer Program

Reward, encourage and acknowledge those special patients who offer you multiple referrals. Every practice has advocates who love them and tell everyone about them. Your office is no different. You have a group of loyal patients who sing your praises every chance they get.

Take care of these special patients. Always send them a handwritten thank you note. Invite them periodically for a complimentary treatment or discounted service, such as a Parisian Peel. Send them a gift basket on their birthday and a special gift during the holidays. It acknowledges you appreciate their support and value their friendship. It will keep them motivated to tell others about you.

Be sure you have a computer system that tracks referrals. It will make this project much easier if it's automated.

> *Resource: www.PatientNOW.com*

## Frequent User/VIP Program

Thanks to the airlines, hotels and coffee shops, patients love frequent user programs. It's a win-win for everyone since it builds patient loyalty for you and makes the frequently visiting patient feel special. Therefore, it makes sense for you to offer your own VIP program. Aesthetic patients today have many choices so you don't want to take them for granted. A true aesthetic patient will see you several times a year and wants to be appreciated for their continued loyalty.

You can use your Vendors' VIP cards specific to their product or you can customize your own, using your own look and feel graphics. And, membership has its perks so be creative. Offer them something special such as:

- Last-minute Appointments
- Free Product Shipping to Their Home
- Makeover After Each Procedure
- Valet Parking
- Free Peel Once a Month, etc.

The point is to make them feel special by appreciating their loyalty. They will, in turn, rave about you to their friends who will also want to be "part of the Club".

> *Resource: www.CosmeticImageMarketing.com*

## Gift Certificates

To help spread word-of-mouth referrals offer attractive gift certificates. Your patients who need a quick gift will love their ease. Their friends, family and colleagues will love the unique gift. Have a gorgeous display in your reception area and at your checkout counter prompting them to add one to their order for the day since it's so convenient. Offer to package it with your office's gift bag and tissue paper. It's the perfect no-hassle gift.

And be sure to remind your patients you offer gift certificates through your newsletters, email marketing, website and any direct mail you send to your patients. Remember: it's not just the initial sale you are interested in, it's the new patient introduced to your practice. The patient may spend hundreds and thousands of dollars with you for years to come as well as refer their own friends, family and colleagues.

> *Resource: www.CosmeticImageMarketing.com*

# IN HOUSE SEMINARS

Coordinate an evening of fun and education. Serve refreshments and show a 30-40 minute power point presentation on what's new in the world of cosmetic enhancement. Use lots of before/after pictures and allow plenty of time for questions and answers. You can mail out a nicely printed invitation to your patients, send an email message and/ or put an ad in your local newspaper. Also, blow up your invitation and display it in your reception area and lobby (if permissible). Be sure to include, "Bring a Friend" to your invitation to encourage your patients to bring their friends, family and colleagues.

It's important to invite any strategic alliances you have such as neighboring hair salons, spas and retail businesses sharing your same demographics. Give them invitations to give to their clients and customers. You may even want to co-market the event by letting them give a short talk and, in return, they will invite their database.

Hold these in-house seminars two to six times per year. And talk with your vendors about sponsoring the event. They are more than willing to help you promote their products and services and may be able to offer you financial support, samples and brochures.

## OPEN HOUSE

The purpose of the Open House is to thank your current patients for their patronage, to reacquaint you with old patients whom you haven't seen for awhile, to increase your word-of-mouth referrals as well as to cross promote your aesthetic services and procedures.

An Open House is a fun evening event for your patients, their friends, family and colleagues, your neighbors and any other alliances you have or want to make. This is a party with wine, food, product samples and gift baskets. It should also include discounted pricing for that evening only. The physician should have a separate space for mini-presentations and the vendors should be on hand to answer questions about their products and services.

Mail out invitations to your current patient database and be sure to add "Bring a Friend", email an invitation, put an ad in your local newspaper, blow up the invitation and display it in your reception area and lobby and invite everyone you come in contact with.

> *Resource: How To Hold A Successful Open House guidebook, dvd, and design files. Part 5 of the How To: Series*
>
> *Visit: www.cosmeticimagemarketing.com/noriskoffer*

## RETENTION ITEMS

Retention items or *"tchotchkes"* reinforce the visibility and image of your practice to your referral sources, patients, prospective patients and the entire community. Since they carry your practice name, telephone number and website address, they are a wonderful way to achieve this visibility. Promotional items help to build your name recognition and can be handed out at your events, speaking engagements – everywhere! Here are some ideas:

- Gel Packs
- Sun Lotion
- Sun Visor
- Face Cloth
- Lip Balm
- Lipstick Holders
- Cosmetic Compact
- Make-up Brushes

- Coffee Mug

- Writing Pad with Pen

- Flower Vase

- Retail Gift Bags with Tissue

> Resource:   www.GioPelle.com
>
>              www.jmppromotionsinc.com

# HOW TO INCREASE YOUR AVERAGE ORDER SIZE

What is often overlooked in the zealous desire to grow the sheer number of patients in your database is the evaluation of a patient's "order size". A true aesthetic patient is interested in looking their best and is open to several procedures, treatments and products that will have them looking their best. So, if they come to you for one particular procedure, there's a very good chance they are also interested in other aesthetic procedures you offer. I guarantee you, if you are not promoting your own treatments and products, the cosmetic counter at the department store down the street and the infomercial on TV are promoting their own, lesser grade treatments and products and your patient is giving them hundreds of dollars at a time.

You can increase your average order size with each patient by:

- Cross promoting comparable aesthetic services to give them a "WOW" result. For example, when they buy Botox and a wrinkle filler, they get a free Parisian Peel treatment. Now, they are experiencing three different modalities working

161

together and they will most likely love the result and be back for more.

- Using technology to treat additional body parts such as hands, chest, arms and legs. Laser hair removal is a good choice because if they have a hair issue on one body part, they probably have it on another.

- Demonstrating a procedure such as Parisian Peel while they are in for their Botox treatment.

- Include a free sample of a product to introduce them to your retail line when they purchase a package of treatments.

Your goal should be to become your aesthetic patient's choice for all their skin care needs. The more your patients visit and see you, the more loyal they will become. Offer them a total solution: retail, skin-care treatments and minimally-invasive as well as surgical procedures to help them look their best so they will return to you again and again.

Resource: www.ParisianPeel.com

## EXTERNAL MARKETING STRATEGIES

In order to build your name recognition as well as your patient database, you want to go out into your community so everyone knows you exist. The more the prospective patient hears your name and sees you, the more familiar you become to them. Thus, the better chance they will call you when they are ready for cosmetic enhancement.

## Advertising

Note: Before advertising, check the AMA code of ethics as well as your own state medical board for their guidelines on medical advertising. The AMA Code of Ethics section E-5.02 states:

"There are no restrictions on advertising by physicians except those that can be specifically justified to protect the pubic from deceptive practices. A physician may publicize him- or herself as a physician through any commercial publicity or other form of public communication (including any newspaper, magazine, telephone directory, radio, television, direct mail, or other advertising) provided that the communication shall not be misleading because of the omission of necessary material information, shall not contain any false or misleading statement, or shall not otherwise operate to deceive."

Media advertising can provide excellent avenues for exposure if done correctly by producing a positive Return on Investment (ROI). It should also:

- Get your telephone to ring

- Attract new patients

- Remind current patients you are around

- Increase your name recognition

- Increase your credibility

- Reinforce your current patient's choice in picking you as their aesthetic physician

An advertising campaign's success is driven by three factors:

- Reach the right people

- The right amount of times

- With the right message

Survey your patients to determine what they read, watch and listen to so you have a better idea where to spend your advertising dollars. For instance, your older patients may watch the local TV station and your younger patients may get their information on the Internet or in social magazines. Find out before you invest in external advertising. Use objective media-buy professionals who know the market and the industry well but are not tied to one outlet.

Resource: www.BurkeMarketing.net

## Yellow Pages

Yellow Pages have always been a favorite medium for physicians. Today with the Internet and other mediums available, most aesthetic patients do not turn to the Yellow Pages for information about a face-lift or a Botox treatment. I suggest using the Yellow Pages or Valley Pages to list your name, telephone number, street address and web address. This way, you are still easy to find and you can transfer your financial resources elsewhere for better exposure.

## Public Relations (PR)

Do you want your name in lights? Do you want to be *"Oprah's go-to-aesthetic doctor"*? Do you want to be quoted in Vogue? Just know the physicians you see on popular television shows and in the high-end magazines have probably paid thousands of dollars per month to savvy PR agencies who have the right contacts to make that happen.

Media are bombarded with thousands of requests each day so the competition is fierce. It takes time, money and expertise to be the "chosen one" for media outlets. Ask yourself if that choice gets your telephone to ring. It certainly massages your ego. However, is the consumer reading, watching or listening really going to travel 2,000 miles to see you for a Botox treatment?

If you want your telephone to ring, think local. Get to know your own local editors, producers and beauty writers whom you can find simply by visiting the media websites. The number of contacts will be manageable and you can keep a list of their telephone numbers, addresses, email addresses and fax numbers handy to contact them with newsworthy stories.

The media are hungry for information of interest to their readers, viewers and listeners. Send them press releases or call them with human-interest ideas. Send them a quality press kit outlining your credentials, areas of expertise, photo and before/after pictures of your 'WOW' results. You can even offer to write a monthly cosmetic column for them at no charge.

PR takes persistence but it can really pay off since it's the most credible source of information about you. I advise you, though, to use professionals if you don't have the time or interest to do it yourself.

Resource: www.CosmeticImageMarketing.com

## Dinner Seminars

Another way to grow your practice with new patients is to hold dinner seminars at a neighborhood restaurant or hotel. Invite the local women for an evening of fun, food and education about the interesting topic of cosmetic enhancement.

You can purchase a mailing list and send out invitations or a seminar service can handle it for you. Keep in mind, however, this is a cold mailing and these women don't know you. You need the free dinner to warm them up to attend. It's a two-hour event where they first have dinner. You then make a presentation for 40-50 minutes, take questions and have your staff available to book consultations on the spot.

Be sure to have a drawing for some complimentary services so you can collect their names and contact information. This also helps to ensure they visit your office to redeem their prize and further bond with you to become a loyal patient.

Dinner seminars are a great opportunity for you to interact with prospective patients one-on-one so they get comfortable with you and trust you to the point they want to see you again. If you don't have the time or the resources to put this together yourself, you can have a service handle the details for you.

Resource: www.Kdunn.com

## Alliances/Networking

One of the fastest and easiest ways to build your practice is through alliances with others who share your same patient demographics. They should include:

- Hair Salons and Spas

- Health Clubs/Personal Trainers

- Women's Clubs

- Retail Shops

- Chambers of Commerce

- Non-Competing Physicians

- Other health care professionals

Join organizations, attend events and speak to groups. By aligning with others, you can be introduced to that group's patients, customers, clients and members. This gives you instant credibility as well as access to new patients.

Cross promote your services, invite them to your events and offer to speak at their events. Give them your business cards to display and hand out. Add a link from your website to their website. Encourage them to introduce you through their newsletter and email marketing efforts to their database.

Always have your business cards readily available so you can hand them out whenever you are in public. You never know who will become your biggest advocate. Also, be sure your staff has business cards as well. Encourage them to hand out their cards to their friends and acquaintances.

Be sure everyone crossing your path knows you and what you offer.

## Speaking Opportunities

There are endless opportunities for you to speak throughout your community. The beauty (pun intended) of speaking to outside groups is the instant credibility you receive. An invitation and introduction from someone will give you instant credibility to their members, patients and clients. And, not only do you get free promotional value by having your name printed on the invitation and in the program, but the face-to-face time with prospective patients is invaluable. And you are tapping into someone else's database to help you grow your own database with new prospective patients.

## Fundraisers

Getting involved in your community is a great way to grow your practice. It shows you care about your fellow man, have compassion and want to make things better in your area.

Offer a silent auction "Beauty Basket." Put together a pretty gift basket full of products and two gift certificates for a non-medical procedure such as a Parisian Peel (one for the winner and one for her friend). Bidding on the prize will help raise money for charity. Make it impressive and colorful so it catches the attendees' eyes so they place a bid. In return, you will receive promotional value such as your name in the invitation that is mailed throughout the community; a mention in the program and you can attend the event to network.

## Direct Mail to New Prospective Patients

If you need to grow your database you can use direct mail, otherwise affectionately known as "junk mail" but be smart about it. You want to:

- Determine the demographics you are interested in attracting to your practice;

- Make it eye-catching and interesting;

- Give them a great offer they can't refuse; and

- Be persistent and consistent.

Since the recipients of your mailing don't know you, it will take repetition to get them to *"stop-notice-act."* Plan to send your direct mail piece to the same people repeatedly. They will feel as if they know you after awhile and will call you when they are finally ready for your services. If they are not ready now, they may be 3-6-12 months from now so keep your name in front of them.

List brokers can give you very specific databases in terms of age, income, ethnicity and geography so be very specific about who your preferred patient is. You don't want to waste money sending information to the wrong audience.

---

Resource: *www.USAData.com*

---

# X

# SELLING RETAIL

Retail can be a healthy revenue stream for your practice. You only have so many hours per day to physically see patients. Adding retail can add to your patient's "order size," which in turn grows your revenues with minimal effort on your part.

The point is to create a patient relationship so strong your patients come to you for all of their aesthetic needs. This means skin care, products, treatments and procedures. Retail is also a great way to build patient loyalty and relationships since they need to return to you again and again for refills.

Be assured, if they are not buying their skin care products from you, they are spending hundreds of dollars at cosmetic counters in department stores. Let them know you offer them a better value of medical-grade products at a comparable cost.

Advantages to Selling Retail:

- New revenue stream

- Increases the average order size of a patient visit

- Increases patient loyalty since they return for refills

- Cross promotes your other services

- Increases your word-of-mouth referrals

- No risk compared to medical procedures

- Introduces your younger patients to cosmetic enhancement now so they come back to you for the more aggressive treatments later

Now, the downside to selling retail:

- Initial cash outlay tied up in inventory

- "Missing" inventory

- Takes up valuable space

- Takes extra time for the physician and staff to talk about products

- Can be perceived as "hard sales" by patients feeling pressured to buy

- Returned and damaged goods

- Allergic reactions can hurt your credibility and patient trust

It is also important to note retail does not sell itself. It takes dedication and a willing staff to promote retail. Your staff needs to be educated not only about the products but the science of skin as well as sales skills. The vendors are happy to help you promote their products. They can offer you additional marketing support with samples, special offers, event support and staff training through lunch-and-learn programs.

Here are some helpful hints for selling retail in your practice:

- Display products in aesthetically-pleasing display cases in the reception area and exam rooms so the patients can see them;

- Provide testers and samples so the patients can touch and feel them;

- Keep it simple: 1-2 skin care lines, mineral makeup and a good sun block;

- Let your vendors help you with lunch-n-learn programs, marketing help and samples;

- Offer your staff incentives for selling retail;

- Use retail to cross promote other services; i.e., free sun block with every laser treatment;

- Sell retail on your website to increase traffic;

- Be sure to keep a tight inventory control and display in locked cases so products don't walk away.

To keep things simple, you may want to hire an aesthetician to handle the entire process of ordering, selling and managing this revenue stream. Be sure, however, if you carry retail, you are committed to turning it into a viable profit center in your practice.

Resource: www.GioPelle.com

www.WWWEnterprise.com

www.ParisianPeel.com

# ON-LINE WEB STORE

You may want to sell retail products on your website. It will help you with search engine optimization and it will help attract traffic to your website. It will also increase the number of patients who return to your website for refills. Professionals can set up the entire online store for you.

Resource: www.WWWEnterprise.com

# PRIVATE LABELING SKIN CARE PRODUCTS

Private or Customized Labeling puts your own name on a skin care line of products. This can increase your name recognition, referrals as well as patient loyalty because they return to you again and again for refills. It can also differentiate you from your competitors and can give you added prestige and a sense of exclusivity. Be sure to work with a reputable manufacturer who offers top grade ingredients.

Resource: www.GioPelle.com

# TRACKING RESULTS

Believe it or not, not every marketing project is a huge success. And not every patient who boasts about sending "tons" of his or her friends to you really do. You cannot truly know what is going on in your practice unless you have accurate facts and figures in front of you.

You need to track results. You need quantifiable data to help you determine what is working, what needs to be "tweaked" and what to discontinue. You need to know which procedures are most profitable and what activities lead to the most booked consultations. It's imperative for everything to be tracked. You need to know where you are, certain trends, conversion rates and any other useful information to help you make better business decisions.

> *You can't fix what you don't know and you don't know if it is not tracked!*

You need to track everything:

- Who calls (new prospective patient or current patient)?

- How did they hear about your practice?

- What prompted the call?

- Converted calls to booked appointments.

- Converted appointments to procedures, treatments or purchases.

- Average order size.

- No-shows and from where.

- Referrals.

- Results per marketing project:

  How many responded?

  How many converted?

  How much revenue versus the cost of the project?

Invest in a good software program that can easily track for you and produce reports outlining the above. You really need to know what works and what does not.

> Resource: www.PatientNOW.com
>
> www.MyMedLeads.com

# RESULTS AND EXPECTATIONS

Be patient. You must allow time for your efforts to work because:

- one ad is not enough;

- one talk is not enough;

- one direct mail piece is not enough.

Your consistent and persistent ads, talks, mailings and other efforts over time will grow your practice. Remember, this is a building process that takes months and years of effort.

# CONCLUSION

Consistent interaction with your preferred patient base builds your foundation for a successful aesthetic practice.

The most successful aesthetic physicians tailor their consultations to the specific needs and wants of each patient. They build rapport by using touch, commonalities, mirroring and active listening. The physician and each staff member understand they are in sales as much as the practice of medicine. They treat the patients as family and regularly keep in touch. They also understand marketing is a process and not an event. They consistently and persistently communicate with their current and prospective patients.

Keep in mind, however, that you cannot please all patients all the time. You also cannot be everything to everybody - do your best to connect with as many patients as possible. Patients are a fickle, emotional group. Don't take it too seriously when they choose your competitor (unless it happens often.)

Think of this as a game. Enjoy it. Do your best, but keep the proper perspective if and when things go wrong – and they will at times. Care – but not too much. You'll win some and lose some. If nothing else, this perspective will take the pressure off you and allow you to enjoy life more, have less stress and get better results. You will have a better attitude and the patients will respond to you more favorably.

Always remember to be yourself (the one in a good mood) and your patients will most likely respond accordingly.

Use the insights, the ideas as well as the resources in this book to grow your aesthetic practice. Marketing is about strategizing AND executing. So develop a plan to attract and retain patients and follow through.

Good luck to you. Perhaps our paths will cross some day.

*Catherine*

# ABOUT CATHERINE MALEY, MBA

As an aesthetic marketing consultant, an aging baby boomer, small business owner and a professional female with a strong career background in sales and marketing, Catherine is in a unique position to understand the needs of the aesthetic patient as well as the wants of an aesthetic physician.

Catherine is a regular contributor to the top medical publications in the industry. She shares the podium with the leaders in aesthetic medicine at national and regional medical meetings throughout the United States and Canada and she consults with numerous private practices and corporations working within the industry.

Her firm Cosmetic Image Marketing (CIM) specializes in growing aesthetic practices using PR, advertising and customized marketing strategies. CIM works with physicians to set goals and map out marketing plans to get the most out of a physician's time, money and resources. CIM has worked with countless practices to cost- effectively market their practices while getting a solid return-on-investment (ROI).

Her education and expertise includes an MBA from the University of San Francisco and a BS degree in Marketing from Golden Gate University, also in San Francisco. She has 19 years of sales and marketing experience with Fortune 500 companies Pitney Bowes and Burlington Northern as well as three years experience with two dot-com start-ups.

Catherine started her career as the House of Delegates Coordinator for the Illinois State Medical Society and the Administrative Director for Specialties with the California Medical Association.

# RESOURCES IN REVERSE ALPHABETICAL ORDER

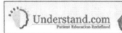
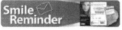

Parisian Peel® is the leading microdermabrasion equipment on the market. As an originator of microdermabrasion in the US we have helped top doctors, medical spas and skin care professioals establish successful aesthetic practices. Through ongoing research Parisian Peel developed the Elite Suffusion™ system with the exclusive ReVisage™ Cellular Restoration Gel, the only clinically proven topical penetration system to show an increase in both Type I and Type III collagen.

Parisian Peel remains at the forefront of aesthetic medicine and has established the highest quality and most reliable aesthetic equipment on the market with complete customer support, on-site service and full marketing program to ensure your success.

**www.parisianpeel.com**

A comprehensive lead management tool for the medical industry that captures, manages, and converts prospects to patients. The MyMedLeads.com tool helps manage all inquiries (online & phone) so that you capture 100% of your prospects. It measures the key response time of your staff, offers text message reminders to prevent no-shows, provides ROI reporting on all marketing expenditures, syndicates online reviews of your medical practice and provides automated email campaigns per procedure to effectively nurture prospects. It easily integrates with the doctor's website as well as directory sites so there is no need for data entry.

**www.MyMedLeads.com**

A leader in web design and development, MedNet Technologies hosts and manages websites for more than 2,500 medical professionals throughout the United States and internationally. Our clients include many of the current and former presidents, past- presidents, officers and directors of prestigious societies and associations such as the American Society of Plastic Surgeons, The American Society for Aesthetic Plastic Surgery, The American Board of Plastic Surgery and the American Academy of Dermatology.

MedNet's dedication to both technical and artistic excellence ensures that each website developed effectively targets their client's desired patient base and is optimized within the search engines to direct appropriate web traffic to their practice.

**www.MedNet-Tech.com**

# RESOURCES BY TOPIC

Marketing only counts if you execute effective strategies to grow your practice. While you and your staff have good intentions, experience hasshown few practices follow through with their marketing efforts. There are many vendors available to help you execute your marketing strategies. Use their expertise and resources to save you time, money and aggravation when growing your aesthetic practice:

| | |
|---|---|
| Aesthetic Marketing Tools: | www.CosmeticImageMarketing.com |
| Before/After Photographs: | www.ProfectMedical.com |
| Camouflage Kits: | www.GioPelle.com |
| Complexion Analysis System: | www.ProfectMedical.com |
| Computer Imaging: | www.UnitedImaging.com |
| Consulting Services: | www.CosmeticImageMarketing.com |
| Cosmetic Questionnaire: | www.CosmeticImageMarketing.com/cosmeticsurvey |
| Customized Practice Poster: | www.CosmeticImageMarketing.com |
| Customized Practice Video: | www.NCPProductions.com<br>www.PracticeProfi tsMedia.com |
| Dinner Seminars: | www.KDunn.com |
| Direct Mail Lists: | www.USAData.com |
| DVD Video Brochures: | www.WaitMediaGroup.com |
| Email Marketing: | www.CosmeticImageMarketing.com |
| Frequent User Cards: | www.NeoMerchant.com |
| Gel Packs/Personalized: | www.GioPelle.com |
| Gift Certificates: | www.CosmeticImageMarketing.com |
| Human Relations Books: | The Art of Persuasion, author, Juliet Erickson<br>How to Make Friends and Influence People, author, Dale Carnegie |
| Implants/Face and Body: | www.Implantech.com |
| Invitations: | www.CosmeticImageMarketing.com |
| Lead Management: | www.MyMedLeads.com |

| | |
|---|---|
| Magazine Advertising: | www.RadiantLifeMagazine.com |
| Marketing Materials: | www.CosmeticImageMarketing.com |
| Mass Media Advertising: | www.BurkeMarketing.net |
| Marketing Ready-Made Tools: | www.CosmeticImageMarketing.com |
| Meet the Doctor: | www.CosmeticImageMarketing.com/meetthedoctor |
| Microdermabrasion: | www.ParisianPeel.com |
| On-Hold Messaging: | www.WaitMediaGroup.com |
| Online Learning Modules: | www.Understand.com<br>www.WaitMediaGroup.com |
| Online Patient Education: | www.Understand.com<br>www.WaitMediaGroup.com |
| Online Patient Communications: | www.SmileReminder.com |
| Online Web Store: | www.WWWEnterprise.com |
| Pain Solutions: | www.GioPelle.com (Gel packs)<br>www.CreativeInc.biz (Zcaine)<br>www.FerndaleLabs.com (LMX)<br>www.GebauerCo.com (Pain Ease) |
| Patient Education: | www.Understand.com<br>www.WaitMediaGroup.com |
| Patient Financing: | www.CareCredit.com |
| Patient Relationship Software: | www.PatientNow.com<br>www.MyMedLeads.com |
| Patient Satisfaction Survey: | www.CosmeticImageMarketing.com/patientsurvey |
| Photography System: | www.ProfectMedical.com |
| Post-Op Healing Solutions: | www.Implantech.com (makers of Cimeosil and GelZone Wrap)<br>www.Procyte.com (makers of Cu3 Crème)<br>www.GioPelle.com |
| Post-Op Surgery Survey: | www.CosmeticImageMarketing.com/postopsurvey |
| Practice Assessment: | www.CosmeticImageMarketing.com |
| PR Slicks: | www.CosmeticImageMarketing.com/prslicks |
| Practice Management Software: | www.PatientNow.com |
| Practice Newsletter: | www.CosmeticImageMarketing.com |
| Practice Video: | www.NCPProductions.com<br>www.PracticeProfitsMedia.com |
| Private Label Skin Products: | www.GioPelle.com |
| Procedure Picture Frames: | www.CosmeticImageMarketing.com |

| | |
|---|---|
| Procedure Videos: | www.WaitMediaGroup.com<br>www.Understand.com |
| Receptionist Training: | www.CosmeticImageMarketing.com |
| Retail Web Store: | www.WWWEnterprise.com |
| Scar Management: | www.Implantech.com (makers of Cimeosil and GelZone Wrap) |
| Search Engine Optimization: | www.MedNet-Tech.com<br>www.EtnaInteractive.com |
| Skin Analysis Software: | www.ProfectMedical.com |
| Skin Care Solutions: | www.ParisianPeel.com<br>www.WWWEnterprise.com<br>www.GioPelle.com |
| Staff Training: | www.CosmeticImageMarketing.com |
| Telephone Tracking Form: | www.CosmeticImageMarketing.com/phonelog |
| Telephone Staff Training: | www.CosmeticImageMarketing.com |
| Thank You Notes: | www.CosmeticImageMarketing.com |
| Tracking Software: | www.PatientNow.com<br>www.MyMedLeads.com |
| Website Design: | www.MedNet-Tech.com<br>www.EtnaInteractive.com |
| Website Lead Tracking: | www.MyMedLeads.com |
| Website Retail Store: | www.WWWEnterprise.com |

# Tools You Need To Stand Out As A Top Aesthetic Practice

## Exceptional Receptionist Guide Book and Flip Chart

Exceptional Receptionist Guide Book and Flip Chart

Turn your receptionist into a profitable gateway to you and your practice. Since the caller will never meet you unless they get past the receptionist, be sure she is equipped to handle the calls effectively.

The Exceptional Receptionist Guide Book and Flip Chart gives her the exact words to say to:

- Bond with the caller
- Qualify them to see where they are at in their decision
- Answer their inquiries effectively and
- Close the appointment

The guide book provides proven phrases that work and a flip chart to use as a "cheat sheet" for a quick reference while on the telephone with prospective patients.

**Call (877) 339-8833 or Visit www.CosmeticImageMarketing.com To Order Today!**

# Tools You Need To Stand Out As A Top Aesthetic Practice

## Staff Sales Scripting For Success

Staff Sales Scripting For Success

**Increase your closing ratios.** It takes skill to direct a prospective patient from being interested in your services to actually booking and paying for your procedures. Learn the sales process skills needed to professionally and effectively guide your prospective patient through the consultation that results in revenues. The guide book will give you the exact words to say during each step of the sales process needed to:

- Build rapport with the prospective patient so they trust and open up to you
- Address their concerns so they trust you are the perfect choice for them
- Promote your uniqueness so they see you as the only viable choice
- Close  profitable procedures

Audio CD's narrated by Catherine Maley are included for your convenience to demonstrate the phrases as they should be said so you learn not only what to say but how to say it.

**Call (877) 339-8833 or Visit www.CosmeticImageMarketing.com
To Order Today!**

# Tools You Need To Stand Out As A Top Aesthetic Practice

## 50 Ways To Attract More Aesthetic Patients

50 Ways To Attract More Aesthetic Patient

This "Plug and Play" system gives you our **Top 50 "Secret" marketing strategies** that are proven to work. Each strategy is explained, an example is shown and you even get the original design files* so you can plug in your contact information and you're done. Learn strategies that can be applied now for immediate results as well as long term strategies for comprehensive practice growth. Marketing doesn't get any easier than this.

### CASE STUDY: Secret Strategy #35
**RESULTS:**

$30,634 In Sales
175 Attendees
52 Procedures Booked
14 Booked Surgical Consultations
26 New Patients

## Call (877) 339-8833 or Visit www.CosmeticImageMarketing.com To Order Today!

# Tools You Need To Stand Out As A Top Aesthetic Practice

## Aesthetic Profits How To: Series

Aesthetic Profits How To: Series

Collect The Secrets to Successful Marketing...They are all right here to make you stand out from your competitors. Easy to use, easy to archive, Aesthetic Profits™ How To: Series™ gives you the tools to stand out from the rest. Explore one profit-making topic in-depth each month. Includes audio-visual and PowerPoint presentations, educational guidebook and four professionally designed strategic marketing templates — just plug in your info and you're done!

**Topics Revealed Include:**

- How To Differentiate Yourself From All The Others
- How To Coordinate A Successful Open House
- How To Advertise To Get Your Phones To Ring
- How To Build A Word-of-Mouth Practice
- How to See a Surge of Patients in 30 Days
- How to Sell Retail Profitably In Your Practice
- How to Effectively Use Email Marketing
- How to Turn Phone Calls Into Profits
- And Many More...

**Call (877) 339-8833 or Visit www.CosmeticImageMarketing.com To Order Today!**

# Tools You Need To Stand Out As A Top Aesthetic Practice

## Consulting To Help Your Practice Succeed

You have holes and leaks in your bucket! Your bucket being your practice and the holes being all the little things you and your staff do to drive patients away from saying YES to you.

With fresh eyes, Catherine identifies where the mistakes are being made and where the thousands of dollars are being left on the table that you don't see because you are too close to the situation.

Catherine's onsite visit to your practice would be priceless. Her assessment and training will give you:

- Better phone conversions

- Better consultation conversions

- More patient referrals

- Much smoother processes

**Call (877) 339-8833 or Visit www.CosmeticImageMarketing.com To Order Today!**

Made in the USA
San Bernardino, CA
06 January 2015